D1258791

Middle School Math
You Really Need

Robert Gardner

and

Edward A. Shore

J. WESTON
WALCH
PUBLISHER
Portland, Maine

User's Guide
to
Walch Reproducible Books

As part of our general effort to provide educational materials which are as practical and economical as possible, we have designated this publication a "reproducible book." The designation means that purchase of the book includes purchase of the right to limited reproduction of all pages on which this symbol appears:

Here is the basic Walch policy: We grant to individual purchasers of this book the right to make sufficient copies of reproducible pages for use by all students of a single teacher. This permission is limited to a single teacher, and does not apply to entire schools or school systems, so institutions purchasing the book should pass the permission on to a single teacher. Copying of the book or its parts for resale is prohibited.

Any questions regarding this policy or requests to purchase further reproduction rights should be addressed to:

Permissions Editor
J. Weston Walch, Publisher
321 Valley Street • P. O. Box 658
Portland, Maine 04104-0658

1   2   3   4   5   6   7   8   9   10

ISBN 0-8251-3283-5

Contents

Chapter 4   **Math with Big and Significant Numbers**

Chapter 5   **Math and Food**

Chapter 6   **Math in Many Places**

Chapter 7   **Math in Art and Music**

Introduction

In writing this book our goal was to provide a variety of real-world situations that would serve as a source of mathematical questions for middle-grade students. We wanted these youngsters to realize that mathematics really is used in solving problems that they are likely to encounter in their own lives.

At the same time, we were constantly guided by the standards recommended by the National Council of Teachers of Mathematics and by our desire to meet the needs of teachers who use cooperative learning in their classrooms. As a result, you will find that much of the material in this book fosters the ideas and suggestions found in *Curriculum and Evaluation Standards for School Mathematics* (1989), recommended by the working groups of the Commission on Standards for School Mathematics of the National Council of Teachers of Mathematics. In particular, we have used "problem solving as a means as well as a goal of instruction," as recommended in the *Standards*. We have certainly tried to encourage the active involvement of students in making use of mathematics; we have suggested cooperative approaches to learning so that students can teach one another and learn from one another; we have encouraged students to communicate ideas through discussion and writing as well as by calculations; and we have assumed that students will make use of pocket calculators to avoid tedious calculations.

Cooperative Learning

The National Council of Teachers of Mathematics' *Curriculum and Evaluation Standards for School Mathematics* for middle grade students includes the statement, "Working in small groups provides students with opportunities to talk about ideas and listen to their peers, enables teachers to interact more closely with students, takes positive advantage of the social characteristics of the middle school student, and provides opportunities for students to exchange ideas and hence develops their ability to communicate and reason." A number of studies have shown that students who work together achieve more and are more capable of solving problems. They are also more helpful to, and caring of, one another and develop better self-esteem and social skills. These studies also reveal that tutoring benefits both tutor and tutee and increases time spent on a task, which is probably the most important factor in learning.

In most professions today, be it business, science, publishing, medicine, or whatever, the problems encountered are complex and arriving at their solutions requires cooperative efforts. Since students will enter a workplace where cooperation is essential, cooperative learning would seem an appropriate approach to use in schools.

Teachers and Cooperative Learning

This book was written with the assumption that the children using it would be working in cooperative groups. We have assumed that the groups will be made up of four students who are frequently broken into pairs. We chose four as a group size because it offers twice as many ways to form pairs (6) as does a group of three; it allows for a group consisting of one high achiever, two medium ability students, and one low achiever, and it avoids the "odd man out" situation. Such an arrangement gives you, the teacher, the potential for a teaching aide (the high-achiever) for each group.

Of course, as teacher, you know the children and their needs better than we do. Consequently, you may decide on a different group size or structure if you use cooperative learning. If you prefer to have students work individually rather than in groups, you can still make use of the problems provided in this book. All you need do is cover the initial instructions to students when you make copies of the pages that contain problems.

Choosing Groups

One way to establish groups for cooperative learning is for you to assign students so that each group has the diversity in ability mentioned above. As the one who best knows the students, you can probably establish groups that will work well together. In addition to ability, you probably will want to ensure that the groups are diverse with regard to gender, race, and ethnicity as well.

On the other hand, you may prefer to give students some role in the selection process. One way to do this is to take aside the top quarter of the class in terms of ability and tell them that they are going to be captains of new work groups. Give them the names of the students who are in the lowest achievement quarter and tell them they are each to choose one person from that group. Then the two members of each growing group can select members from among the remaining average ability students. You will probably want to establish some restrictions to ensure that groups contain both boys and girls as well as racial and ethnic diversity.

Our Choice of Problems

By choosing problems from a variety of sources, we have tried to make students aware of the connections between mathematics and ordinary life activities. Although most students recognize the role of mathematics as a valuable tool for the scientist and engineer, they seldom realize the role that mathematics plays in sports, travel, music, art, money, household activities such as cooking and buying paint and lumber, making everyday estimates, and so on.

We hope that the questions found between these covers will lead students to realize that mathematics is valuable in solving real problems that arise during the course of most lives—a realization that may motivate them to pursue mathematics with greater intensity. Further motivation will come from doing the analyses required by the problems, comparing solutions, and questioning one another as to whether or not the answers seem reasonable.

As you can see from the table of contents, we have chosen a variety of sources to show how math is used in everyday life or in answering interesting questions. As former teachers, we know how difficult it is to find time to write questions or develop problem situations that will both challenge and motivate students. We hope you will find that many of these problems meet your needs, are appropriate for your students, and will help them to see that mathematics can and will play a significant role in their lives.

CHAPTER 1   Math and Money

To the Teacher

Almost everyone realizes that the use of money, even counting pennies, requires some knowledge of mathematics. Because it is the most familiar and common use of mathematics, we made it our opening chapter. Here students will see how math is used in calculating interest, percentage savings on sale items, reading the financial pages, repairing and painting buildings, paying taxes and establishing tax rates, and estimating the operating cost of electrical appliances.

1. Simple and Compound Interest
(page 6)

It is not necessary to teach the exponential formula for compound interest. The student can use the multiplication function of a calculator. The main point here is to understand the *difference* between simple and compound interest. The table called for in questions 2 and 3 clearly illustrates this.

Your students may enjoy preparing interest problems for others to solve. Or you might prepare problems of varying difficulty and give them to students to solve. A very capable student might work on a problem in which interest is compounded monthly, while a less able student works on a simple interest problem.

You might like to follow this section with section 37 (Handheld Calculators) in Chapter 6. That section involves showing students how to use the y^x function on a calculator to determine the growth of money over a number of interest periods.

Answers

1. a. After 6 months: P = $5,000 + ($5,000 × 0.04) = $5,200.

     After 1 year: P = $5,200 + ($5,200 × 0.04) = $5408.

     After 1.5 years: P = $5,408 + ($5,408 × 0.04) = $5,624.32

     After 2 years: P = $5,624.32 + ($5,624.32 × 0.04) = $5,849.29

   b. $5,849.29 – $5,800 = $49.29

2 and 3.

year	@ 7% simple	@ 6 % compound
1	$10,700	$10,600
2	11,400	11,236
3	12,100	11,910 (end 3rd yr, #1)
4	12,800	12,625
5	13,500	13,383
6	14,200	14,186
7	14,900	15,037
8	15,600	15,939 (end 8th yr, #2)

The best choice for a 3-year investment is clearly 7% simple interest.

The best choice for an 8-year investment is 6% compound interest.

2. Where Do You Use Percentage? How About Sales?
(page 8)

Be sure to emphasize that "percentage" simply means "hundredths" in any real calculation.

Avoid questions involving car sales. Car sales are very complicated. They usually involve such factors as the compound interest on the value of the car and any monies transferred, the "rebate," and the dealer's discount . . . factors that are not easy to analyze.

Students can be asked to collect any examples that they find using "percentage" for discussion in class.

Answers

1. $100 – .40($100) = $60.

2. $86.00 – (0.30 × $86.00) = $86.00 – $25.80 = $60.20

3. $400 – $328 = $72; (72/400) × 100 = 18%

4. The presale price was $100. The sale price must be 75%

   (75/100) of the original price, so $\frac{75}{100} = \frac{\$75}{?}$; the only value that will make these two fractions equal when the question mark is replaced with a value is $100.

   If your students have had introductory algebra, the solution is simple:
   $75 = 0.75 \, X$; $X = \$75/0.75 = \$100$

5. a. Yes.

   b. For Misses Contemporary Linen Blend the greatest savings are at the low end of the price range: $68.00 – $19.99 = $48.01; $48.01/

$68.00 = 71%. For the casuals, savings are greatest (63%) at the high end of the price range: $108.00 – $39.99 = $68.01; $68.01/$108 = 63%.

3. Using Math to Read the Newspaper's Financial Pages
(page 10)

Financial pages contain lots of mathematics, but a great deal of economics must also be understood if one is to use them effectively. Here we tackle only some of the simpler concepts—ones that will be found in most financial reporting about stocks.

After completing this section, you might ask students to choose a stock to follow for the rest of the year. During the course of the school year, which student's stock shows the greatest gain? The greatest decrease in value? Which shows the greatest percentage gain? The greatest percentage loss? Are gains in value always accompanied by gains in yield?

Answers

1. As an example, suppose Abac reports a yearly dividend of $0.48 and a closing price of $11.00 per share. The yield is (0.48/11) × 100 = 4.4%. (The paper actually listed 4.2%.)

2. As an example, on one day the paper listed 18,974 under the column "Sales 100s" for Gen El. (General Electric). Therefore, 18,974 must be multiplied by 100 to give 1,897,400 as the number of shares sold that day.

3. The closing price, listed under "Last," might have been $78\frac{1}{4}$ ($78.25).

4. The change from the previous day, listed under "Chg" might have been $-\frac{5}{8}$ (– $0.63) or down five-eighths.

5. Since closing price = previous day's price + change, the previous day's price = last (closing price) – change, or the previous day's price must reflect the change seen in today's price:

Previous day = $78\frac{1}{4} - (-\frac{5}{8}) = 78\frac{1}{4} + \frac{5}{8} = 78\frac{7}{8}$, or since the stock lost $\frac{5}{8}$, it must have been $\frac{5}{8}$ higher on the previous day.

4. Sales! *(page 11)*

This problem clearly shows the penalty paid for not having sufficient cash on hand. By choosing to buy over time, you pay a lot of interest.

Students may enjoy writing their own advertisement problems and asking other groups to solve them. You may or may not choose to edit the problems. Much could be learned by having the students edit the problems they receive before attempting to solve them.

Answers

1. a. Over a five-year period there would be 60 payments of $99 each, for a total of $5940.

2. a. Percent of sales price = $5940/$3995 = 1.49 = 149%, about $1\frac{1}{2}$ times the sale price.

    b. $5940 – $3995 = $1945.

    Clearly, you have to pay almost $2,000 extra in interest for the "privilege" of paying for this piano over five years. If you could have saved first and paid for the piano in cash, (all $4,000), you'd save the $2000 in finance charges.

3. a. The cost of the piano was $3995. Total payments were $5940, or the cost of the piano was 3995/5940 × 100 = 67% of the payments.

    b. The finance charge was $1945, or 1945/5940 × 100 = 33% of the payments.

    c. and d. You paid $1945 in interest or $1945/5 = $389 per year. This is almost 10 % per year ($389/$3995 = .097).

    e. Decisions as to whether or not the interest was reasonable will depend on current rates of interest.

4. The added cost to move the more distant piano will be:

    100 mi × 2 × $0.49/mi + [(200 mi ÷ 12 mi/gal) × $1.40] + 200 mi × $0.30/mi = $98 + $23.33 + $60 = $181.33.

    Since the savings will be $3995 – $3500 = $495, it will cost less money to buy the piano in the more distant city provided it is comparable to the one that is nearby.

5. Buildings and Grounds *(page 12)*

This section involves questions that any family might face if they buy a home that needs painting. It also provides another opportunity for students to see the role that estimates play in making decisions about money.

Answers

1. a. 12 panes/window × 18 windows = 216 panes.

    b. 18 windows × 1.25 hr/window = 22.5 hr.

    c. $\frac{1}{2}$ hr/window × 18 windows = 9 hr.

    d. 22.5 hr + 9 hr = 31.5 hr.

    e. $\frac{6}{18} = \frac{1}{3}$ of the windows, so you will need about twice as much again as you have already used, or 1 can of putty and three quarts ($\frac{3}{4}$ gal) of paint.

f. You used $1\frac{1}{2}$ cans of putty, so you had to buy 2 cans. $2 \times \$2.35 = \$4.70$. Unfortunately, you used $3 \times 1\frac{1}{2}$ quarts of primer paint so you will need $4\frac{1}{2}$ quarts. A gallon (4 qts.) will be a quart less than what you need, so unless you can find a store that sells the same paint in quart or pint quantities, you will have to buy 2 gallons at a cost of $2 \times \$16.95 = \$33.90$. Total cost = $\$33.90 + \$4.70 = \$38.60$.

g. In gallon cans it will cost $2 \times \$18.95 = \$37.90$. In quart cans the cost is $5 \times \$7.45 = \$37.25$. The smart shopper will buy one gallon can and one quart can, which will cost $\$18.95 + \$7.45 = \$26.40$.

2. a. 1800 sq. ft. ÷ 325 sq. ft./gal = 5.54 gal. You will need 6 gallons. This will cost $6 \times \$17.90 = \$107.40$.

b. 1800 sq. ft. ÷ 400 sq. ft./gal = $4\frac{1}{2}$ gal. You will need 5 gallons. This will cost $5 \times \$20.95 = \$104.75$.

6. *Taxes* (page 13)

Property taxes are based on the value of a taxpayer's property, most commonly land and buildings. Tax rates can be expressed in mils; that is, in dollars per thousand dollars of property, which is the same as mils per dollar (0.1¢/$).

You may want to encourage students to obtain information about their town's tax rate, how it is established, and what other sources of revenue your town has. You might invite a local official such as an assessor to explain to your students how they determine property values and establish a tax rate.

Answers

1. a. As indicated on the bill, the tax rate is 11.05/$1000 or 11.05 mils.

b. $39,300 + $104,100 = $143,400

c. $39,300 × 0.01105 = $434.27

d. $104,100 × 11.05/1000 = $1150.31

e. $143,400 × 0.01105 = $1584.57 or $434.27 + $1150.31 = $1584.58

f. An ordinary year is a calendar year, one that extends from January 1 through December 31. A fiscal year is the 12 month period over which an organization plans its finances. In many town governments the fiscal year runs from July 1 of one calendar year through June 30 of the following year.

2. Yes. $55.25/$5000 = 0.01105, or $5000 × 0.01105 = $55.25

3. a. $10,000,000 - ($750,000 + $500,000 + $50,000) = $8,700,000

b. $8,700,000 ÷ $950,000,000 = 0.00916 or 9.16 mil or $9.16 per $1000 of property.

4. The value of a taxpayer's property is established by assessors (town officials). They use guidelines to be fair and treat all citizens alike. This is difficult, of course, because a building's location is often as important as its cost of construction and the area of the land it is on. A beautiful home near a public dump does not have the same value as a comparable home overlooking a lake or ocean.

5. a.

Amount of purchase ($)	Tax ($)
0.10–0.30	0.01
0.31–0.50	0.02
0.51–0.70	0.03
0.71–0.90	0.04
0.91–1.00	0.05
2.00	0.10
3.00	0.15
4.00	0.20

5.00	0.25
10.00	0.50
100.00	5.00
1000.00	50.00

b. The tax from 10¢ to 100¢ is obtained by rounding the tax to the nearest penny. The tax for intermediate values not shown can be easily determined by addition or multiplication of the taxes shown in the table.

c. (1) $1.59 = 5¢ + 3¢ = 8¢
    (2) $6.78 = 25¢ + 5¢ + 4¢ = 34¢
    (3) $ 12.98 = 50¢ + 10¢ + 5¢ = 65¢
    (4) $45.78 = 4 × $0.50 + $0.25 + $0.04 = $2.29
    (5) $576.90 = 5 × $5 + 7 x $0.50 + 6 × $0.05 + $0.05 = $28.85
    (6) $14,760 = 14 × $50 + 7 × $5 + 6 × $0.50 = $738

(7) $160,000 = 160 × $50 = $8000
(8) $1,250,000 = 1,250 × $50 = $62,500

7. *Operating Costs of Electrical Appliances* (page 16)

This section should make students aware of the fact that more is involved in the cost of an appliance than its initial cost. There is a price to be paid for operating any electrical appliance, and that cost depends on the price of electrical energy, which is in cents per kilowatt-hour used, and the time the device is operated. Bear in mind that a kilowatt is a unit of power—a measurement of energy per time. When power is multiplied by time, the product has energy units. Thus, energy/time × time = energy, or, in units, kilowatts (power) × hours (time) = kilowatt-hours (energy).

Once again, students will see the value of being able to make reasonable estimates before making financial decisions.

Answers

You can extend this activity by asking student groups to prepare additional problems involving appliances, then give them to another group to solve.

1. 365 d/y × 24 h/d × $\frac{1}{2}$ × 0.320 kW × 12¢/ kW h = 16,819 ¢ = $168.19/y

2. 4.8 kW × 200 h/y × $0.09/kWh = $86.40/y

3.

Appliance	Wattage (W)	Average use per year (h)	Annual operating cost ($)
Toaster	1200	40	$4.80
Washer	500	300	$15
Water heater	2400	1500	$360
Electric clock	2	8760	$1.75
Radio	60	4000	$24
Light bulbs	750	3000	$225

4. a. Water heater

    b. Clock

5. a. Clock

    b. Water heater

1. Simple and Compound Interest

Banks and various companies will pay you to allow them to use your money for their own purposes. The money they agree to pay you or add to the money you invest is called interest. There are two kinds of interest: simple and compound.

To find simple interest all you have to do is multiply the principal by the rate ($p \times r$). The principal is the amount of money with which you start your investment. For example, a person might have $5,000 to invest. The $5,000 is the principal. He or she finds a company that will guarantee an interest of 8% per year. The rate—the simple interest paid per year—is 8%. At the end of one year, the principal will be worth $5,000 + the interest. The simple interest on $5,000 after one year is:

$$\$5,000 \times .08 = \$400$$

(Notice that 8% has been changed to .08 because 8% means 8/100 or 0.08.)

At the end of one year your money has grown to $5,000 plus the interest of $400, giving a total of $5,400.

At the end of the second year, the principal once again earns 8%, or $400. If you don't spend any of the money, you will now have a total of $5400 + $400 = $5800.

Compound interest is similar but better for the investor. With compound interest, the interest is added to the principal each year (or possibly more often). For example, if $5,000 were invested at 8% compounded annually, then at the end of one year the principal would be worth $5,400. The 8% interest for the second year would be paid on $5,400, not $5,000. At the end of the second year, the principal would have increased to:

$$\$5,400 + (\$5,400 \times 0.08) = \$5,400 + \$432 = \$5,832.$$

As you can see, you are $32 richer with compound interest than with simple interest.

Interest may be compounded more often than once a year. Suppose the company agrees to pay 8% interest compounded semi-annually (every 6 months). At the end of 6 months, the principal will have grown to:

$$\$5,000 + (\$5,000 \times 0.08/2) = \$5,200.$$

At the end of the first year, the principal will be worth:

$$\$5,200 + (\$5200 \times .08/2) = \$5,200 + \$208 = \$5,408.$$

Compounding the interest on an investment makes a big difference when done over a long period of time!

(continued)

           Middle School Math You Really Need

1. Simple and Compound Interest *(continued)*

If you are working in groups, divide into pairs and work individually on problems 1–3. Then check your answers with your partner. After completing and checking the problems go back into your larger group and work out any disagreements you may have.

Your group might like to prepare additional problems on simple and compound interest and give them to another group to solve. Your group can then work on problems you receive from them. Use the back of this page to figure your answer.

1. In the example above, where the 8% interest is compounded semi-annually:

   a. What would the principal be worth after two years?

   b. How much more is this principal than the principal you would have if the $5,000 were invested using simple interest at the same rate?

2. You have a choice; you can invest $10,000 at 7% simple interest for a period of three years, or the same principal at only 6% compounded annually for the same three years. Which investment would you choose and why?

3. What choice would you make if you invested the money for 8 years? (Make a careful table to show the values at the end of each year.)

2. Where Do You Use Percentage? How About Sales?

Stores often announce a sale with an ad that might read: "20% off all dresses!" This means that all dresses are reduced in price by 20% of the pre-sale price. For example, a dress costing $50.00 before the sale is reduced in price to ($50.00 − $0.20 × 50.00) = ($50.00 − $10.00) = $40.00.

Notice that we have written 20% as $0.20 = \frac{20}{100}$.

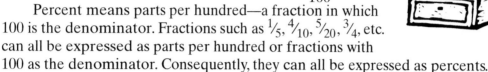

Percent means parts per hundred—a fraction in which 100 is the denominator. Fractions such as $\frac{1}{5}, \frac{4}{10}, \frac{5}{20}, \frac{3}{4}$, etc. can all be expressed as parts per hundred or fractions with 100 as the denominator. Consequently, they can all be expressed as percents.

$$\frac{1}{5} = \frac{20}{100} = 0.20 = 20\%; \quad \frac{4}{10} = \frac{40}{100} = 0.40 = 40\%;$$

$$\frac{5}{20} = \frac{25}{100} = 0.25 = 25\%; \quad \frac{3}{4} = \frac{75}{100} = 0.75 = 75\%.$$

Other fractions such as $\frac{1}{3}, \frac{4}{6}, \frac{5}{8}, \frac{7}{12}$, and others cannot be expressed as even percentages. In these cases, the fraction is converted to a decimal fraction and then to the nearest part per hundred as a percentage.

$$\frac{1}{3} = 0.3333\ldots = 33\%; \quad \frac{4}{6} = 0.666666 = 67\%;$$

$$\frac{5}{8} = 0.625 = 63\%; \quad \frac{7}{12} = 0.583333\ldots = 58\%.$$

In problems that deal with money, percentage is particularly useful because 1¢ is 1% of $1.00 (1¢/100¢ = 0.01 = 1%).

▼ ▼ ▼ ▼ ▼ ▼ ▼ ▼ ▼ ▼ ▼ ▼ ▼ ▼ ▼ ▼ ▼ ▼ ▼ ▼

If you are working in groups, divide into pairs and work individually on problems 1–4. Then check your answers with your partner. After completing and checking the problems, go back into your larger group and work out any disagreements you may have. Repeat the procedure for questions 5–7, which are concerned with advertisements and figuring what to write on sales tags.

Your group might like to prepare additional problems by writing questions related to sales ads that you invent. Give your problems to another group to solve. Your group can then work on problems you receive from the other group. Use the back of this page to figure your answer.

▼ ▼ ▼ ▼ ▼ ▼ ▼ ▼ ▼ ▼ ▼ ▼ ▼ ▼ ▼ ▼ ▼ ▼ ▼ ▼

(continued)

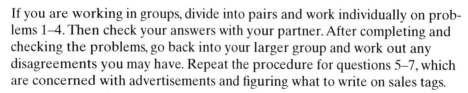

2. Where Do You Use Percentage? How About Sales? *(continued)*

1. A store announces a sale during which all clothes are reduced in price by 40%. What is the sale price of a jacket that cost $100 before the sale?

2. A coat has a list price of $86.00. It is placed on sale at 30% off the list price. What sale price should a clerk attach to the coat?

3. A suit is on sale for $328. Its original price was $400. By what percent has it been reduced in price?

4. What was the original price of a coat that has a sale price of $75 if the sale ads announced "25% savings on all coats"?

5. A very big department store featured an ad in which "separates" were on sale. One part of the ad read:

    > "Misses Contemporary Linen Blend Separates:
    > SAVE 59%–71%
    > Originally $68–$98;
    > our new low prices $19.99–$39.99."

    Another part of the ad read:

    > "Misses Leading Maker Casual Related Separates:
    > SAVE 58%–63%
    > Originally $38–$108;
    > our new low prices $15.99–$39.99."

    a. Do the percentage figures given in the ads agree with the savings indicated by the original and new price ranges?

    b. To obtain the greatest percentage savings should a customer buy items at the low or the high end of the price range?

3. Using Math to Read the Newspaper's Financial Pages

The financial pages of the newspaper are filled with mathematics. Since the New York Times is nationally available, we will use it as a source of financial material. Almost any local paper will give you the same type of information as the Times, but probably with less detail.

Get a copy of the New York Times (not Sunday or Monday edition, which do not report trading for the day), and find the tables that report New York Stock Exchange Issues. Near the head of the tables you will find a box labeled Stock Tables Explained. Notice that "yield" is the annual dividend divided by the closing price. The quotient is then multiplied by 100 so the yield can be expressed as a percentage.

▼ ▼ ▼ ▼ ▼ ▼ ▼ ▼ ▼ ▼ ▼ ▼ ▼ ▼ ▼ ▼ ▼ ▼

If you are working in groups of four, have each person find the yield for one of the four stocks chosen in question 1. Then show the other members of the group how you calculated the yield.

Then divide into pairs and work individually on questions 2–5. Check your answers with your partner. Finally, go back into your larger group, work out any disagreements you may have, then have each member repeat questions 2–5 for the four stocks the group did in question 1. Use the back of this page to figure your answer.

▼ ▼ ▼ ▼ ▼ ▼ ▼ ▼ ▼ ▼ ▼ ▼ ▼ ▼ ▼ ▼ ▼ ▼

1. Choose four stocks from the list. Check the accuracy of their reported yields.

2. Find General Electric (Gen El) on the table. How many shares of General Electric were traded on the date given in the report? (Notice that the head of the column "Sales" notes that sales are in 100's. This means that the reported number must be multiplied by 100.)

3. What was the closing price of Gen El in the paper you have?

4. By how much did the closing price of General Electric differ from the price on the previous day?

5. Use the answers to questions 3 and 4 to find the closing price of General Electric on the previous trading day.

Name _____   Date _____

4. "Sales!"

A recent advertisement for a used Yamaha Baby Grand piano read, "Ebony polish G-2, 10 year guarantee, parts and labor, $3,995 . . . if new, $18,900. Only $99 a month . . . financing up to five years."

As you can see, you could buy the piano for $3,995 if you had that much money. Or you could pay for it over a five-year period by paying $99 per month. The owner indicates that you would have to pay $18,900 for the instrument if you purchased it new in a store.

▼ ▼ ▼ ▼ ▼ ▼ ▼ ▼ ▼ ▼ ▼ ▼ ▼ ▼ ▼ ▼ ▼ ▼ ▼

If you are working in groups, divide into pairs and work individually on problems 1–4. Then check your answers with your partner. After completing and checking the problems, go back into your larger group and work out any disagreements you may have.

▼ ▼ ▼ ▼ ▼ ▼ ▼ ▼ ▼ ▼ ▼ ▼ ▼ ▼ ▼ ▼ ▼ ▼ ▼

1. If you agreed to purchase this piano over a five-year period, what is the total amount of money you would have to pay?

2. a. What percent of the sale price ($3,995) would these payments be?

   b. How much more than the sale price would you have to pay?

3. a. What percent of the total payments would be the cost of the piano?

   b. What percent of the total payments would be the finance charge?

   c. How much interest would you pay if you bought the piano over a five-year period?

   d. What is the average annual interest rate over this five-year period?

   e. Did the seller ask for reasonable interest, or would you be charged an excessive amount for buying over time?

4. You have the money needed to purchase the piano, but you see an ad for an identical instrument in another newspaper. This piano is only $3,500, but it is in a town 100 miles away. You will have to rent a truck at $50 per day to move either piano. However, the truck-rental company also charges 49¢ for every mile that you drive the truck. You also have to pay for gas. The truck will go about 12 miles on one gallon of gas. Gasoline in your area costs about $1.40 per gallon.

   Since you want to examine both instruments before you buy, you will have to drive to the distant city. It costs about 30¢ per mile to operate your car.

   Assuming that you have the time to spare, and a friend who will help you move the piano, which piano would cost less money?

 Middle School Math You Really Need

5. Buildings and Grounds

Your family is thinking about buying an old house, fixing it, and reselling it for a profit. You have been told to collect information about the house.

▼ ▼ ▼ ▼ ▼ ▼ ▼ ▼ ▼ ▼ ▼ ▼ ▼ ▼ ▼ ▼ ▼ ▼

If you are working in groups, divide into pairs and work individually on the two problems that follow. Then meet with your partner to check your answers and work out any disagreements. Finally, meet with the entire group to compare answers and resolve differences. Use the back of this page to figure your answers.

▼ ▼ ▼ ▼ ▼ ▼ ▼ ▼ ▼ ▼ ▼ ▼ ▼ ▼ ▼ ▼ ▼ ▼

1. The windows need to be puttied and painted. You find that each window is divided and holds 12 panes of glass. The house has 18 windows. You estimate that it will take about one hour and 15 minutes to scrape, putty, and apply a coat of primer paint to each window. You think the finish coat of paint will require about 30 minutes per window.

   a. How many window panes are in the house?

   b. How long will it take to scrape, putty, and apply a first coat of paint to all the windows?

   c. How long will it take to apply the second coat of paint to all the windows?

   d. What is your estimate of the total time required to paint all the windows?

   e. After painting 6 windows, you find you have used a quart and a half of primer paint and $\frac{1}{2}$ can of putty. How much more primer paint and putty do you estimate you will need to finish the job?

   f. The putty costs $2.35 per can and the primer paint, which is sold in gallon cans, costs $16.95 per gallon. What was the cost of paint and putty for the prime coat?

   g. The finish coat requires the same amount of paint as the primer coat. The finish coat costs $18.95 per gallon, but it can be bought in quart cans for $7.45 per can. How much will it cost for the finish coat?

2. Now you need to estimate the amount of paint needed to paint the sides of the house. You measure its outside area and find it to be 1800 square feet. At the paint store, you find that a gallon of quality primer paint will cover about 325 square feet and costs $17.90 per gallon. The paint you plan to use for your second coat will cover 400 square feet and costs $20.95 per gallon.

   a. How many gallons of primer should you buy? How much will it cost?

   b. How many gallons of paint should you buy for the second coat? How much will it cost?

Middle School Math You Really Need

6. Taxes

People who own property pay a property tax to the town or county they live in. The tax revenues are used to pay for schools, roads, libraries, police and fire protection, and so on. The tax is determined by the town's estimate (assessment) of the value of the property and the **mil rate** established by the local government. A mil is $\frac{1}{1000}$ of a dollar.

Suppose the mil rate in a certain town is 12.0. This means that property will be taxed $\frac{12}{1000}$ of a dollar for every dollar of value that your property has. A property owner will pay a tax of $12 for every $1000 of property value owned. If your property is assessed at (believed to be worth) $100,000, then your property tax for that year will be:

$$\frac{12}{1000} \times \$100,000 = \$1200.$$

▼ ▼ ▼ ▼ ▼ ▼ ▼ ▼ ▼ ▼ ▼ ▼ ▼ ▼ ▼ ▼ ▼

If you are working in groups, divide into pairs and work together on the four questions that follow. You may have to do some research on question 4. After completing and checking the problems, go back into your larger group and compare results. Then work out any disagreements you may have.

▼ ▼ ▼ ▼ ▼ ▼ ▼ ▼ ▼ ▼ ▼ ▼ ▼ ▼ ▼ ▼ ▼

1. A property-tax bill received by a citizen might look like this. The total value of land and buildings and the total tax columns are shown here as blanks. Normally they show dollars.

Fiscal Year 1996	Commonwealth of Massachusetts Town of Eastwind				Bill No. 7654321	
Tax rate/$1000 11.05						
Location	Land Area	Land value	Bldgs	Bldg. value	Total value	Total tax
See deed xyz 123	0.51	$39,300	1	$104,100	_____	_____

a. What is the mil rate in this town?

b. What is the total value of the property owned by this citizen?

c. What will be the taxes, in dollars, on this citizen's land for fiscal year 1996?

(continued)

　　　　　13　　　　　*Middle School Math You Really Need*

6. Taxes *(continued)*

    d. What will be the taxes, in dollars, on this citizen's house (bldg.) for fiscal year 1996?

    e. What is the total property tax this citizen will pay for fiscal year 1996?

    f. What is the difference between an ordinary year and a fiscal year?

2. The same person owns a car, which is worth $5,000. The citizen receives a separate tax bill of $55.25 for the value of the car. Is the tax rate on the car the same as the tax rate on the land and building?

3. A town expects to spend $10,000,000 during the next fiscal year. It also expects to receive as income $750,000 from the state, $500,000 from fees and permits, and $50,000 from interest on its investments. The rest of its income must come from property taxes. The total value of property owned by citizens in the town is $950,000,000.

    a. How much money must the town obtain from taxes if it is to balance its budget?

    b. What tax rate, in mils (dollars/$1000) should the town set for the coming fiscal year?

4. How are the dollar values for a citizen's property determined?

5. In most states a sales tax is levied on many of the things that you might buy. This includes clothing, cars, hardware, household goods, food bought in a restaurant, and so on. A tax table is placed near the cash registers in some stores so that the clerk can quickly add the sales tax to any items purchased. Some people carry a tax table with them. This way they can easily work out the tax on anything they plan to buy.

    a. Assume that a state has a sales tax of 5% and does not tax sales of less than 10¢. Then complete the table below.

Amount of purchase ($)	Tax ($)	Amount of purchase ($)	Tax ($)
0.10–0.30	0.01	2.00	0.10
0.31–0.50	0.02	3.00	____
0.51–0.70	____	4.00	____
0.71–0.90	____	5.00	____
0.91–1.00	____	10.00	____
		100.00	____
		1000.00	____

(continued)

6. Taxes *(continued)*

b. Why does the table not contain a tax for every penny from 10¢ to 99¢ and for every dollar from $1 to $1000?

c. Use the table to find the sales tax on a purchase of:

(1) $1.59

(2) $6.78

(3) $ 12.98

(4) $45.78

(5) $576.90

(6) $14,760

(7) $160,000

(8) $1,250,000

7. Operating Costs of Electrical Appliances

A century ago, food was kept in an ice box—an insulated box that held a large piece of ice. Food was cooked on a wood- or coal-burning stove made of cast iron. Clothes were washed on a corrugated board, known as a scrub board, and dried on a line in a sunny area or stretched across one end of the kitchen. Dishes were washed in a basin in the sink using water pumped by hand from a well and floors were swept, not vacuumed, with a broom.

Today, life is much easier physically. We have electrical appliances—refrigerators, stoves, washers, dryers, dishwashers, vacuum cleaners, and more. But these appliances come at a price. Not only do we have to buy the appliances, we have to pay for the electrical energy to operate them.

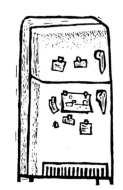

Fortunately, you can make a reasonable estimate of the annual cost to operate any appliance. To do so you need to know three things: (1) The approximate length of time you expect the appliance to be used each year; (2) The appliance's wattage rating (the electrical energy it uses per hour); (3) The cost of the electrical energy supplied by your local power plant in cents per kilowatt-hour.

Suppose you want to know how much it will cost to operate a TV set for a year. Somewhere on the TV set you will find its operating wattage. It might be 200 watts (W) or 0.2 kilowatts (kW) because one kilowatt is equal to 1,000 W. You estimate that the television will be used about four hours per day. You then look at a bill from your power company and find that they charge 10¢ per kilowatt-hour (kWh) of electrical energy used.

The electrical energy needed to operate the TV for one year can now be calculated. Simply multiply the kilowatts of power needed to operate the TV by the number of hours you estimate it will be used.

You can then estimate the operating cost by multiplying the electrical energy needed per year by the cost of the energy in cents per kWh.

(continued)

7. **Operating Costs of Electrical Appliances** (continued)

▼ ▼ ▼ ▼ ▼ ▼ ▼ ▼ ▼ ▼ ▼ ▼ ▼ ▼ ▼ ▼ ▼ ▼

If you are working in groups, divide into pairs and work individually on questions 1 and 2. Then check your answers with your partner. After completing and checking these two questions, go back into your larger group and work out any disagreements you may have.

The larger group can then work together on question 3, where different people can make the calculations for different appliances. However, more than one person should do the calculations for each appliance to serve as a check on one another. Those who did the calculations on the operating costs of each appliance should explain how they arrived at their answers. The group can then settle any differences before collectively answering questions 4 and 5.

▼ ▼ ▼ ▼ ▼ ▼ ▼ ▼ ▼ ▼ ▼ ▼ ▼ ▼ ▼ ▼ ▼ ▼

1. You want to buy a frostless refrigerator. It is rated at 320 W. A salesman tells you that the appliance will probably run half the time. If your power company charges 12¢ per kilowatt-hour, what will it cost to operate this appliance for one year?

2. A clothes dryer operates at a power of 4.8 kW (4800 W). You estimate that it will be used about 200 hours per year (h/y). Bills from your power company show a charge of $0.09/kWh. What is your estimate of the annual operating cost of this appliance?

3. The following table lists several common electrical appliances, their power ratings, and their average hours of operation per year. Electrical energy costs 10¢ per kilowatt-hour. What is the annual cost of operating each appliance?

(continued)

7. Operating Costs of Electrical Appliances *(continued)*

Appliance	Wattage (W)	Average use per year (h)	Annual operating cost ($)
Toaster	1200	40	
Washer	500	300	
Water heater	2400	1500	
Electric clock	2	8760	
Radio	60	4000	
Light bulbs	750	3000	

4. Which of the appliances in the table above:

   a. requires the most power to operate?

   b. requires the least power to operate?

5. Which of the appliances costs:

   a. the least to operate?

   b. the most to operate?

CHAPTER 2   Math for Travelers

To the Teacher

People who are traveling use math to anticipate arrival times, exchange money, make use of both road and weather maps, and convert temperatures and distances to more familiar units. Many who travel do so in their own automobiles. Such people use mathematics when they buy their cars, when they calculate the car's economy in miles per gallon (MPG), when they estimate the cost of a trip, and when they do many other calculations relating to their automobile.

In section 11, students will learn how to measure the shortest distance between two cities that are far apart. They may be surprised to find that the shortest distance is the arc of a circle that does not follow a line of latitude.

8. Change, Cambio, Wechsel: Changing Foreign Currency
(page 24)

In teaching students how to convert from the value of one currency to another, it is important to solve each problem by thinking in terms of the units. This method applies not only to currencies, but to any problem involving units.

Suppose you are in France and you find the exchange rate is F5.45 for a dollar (F is for French francs). This can be written as:

$$\frac{1 \text{ dollar}}{5.45 \text{ francs}} \quad \text{or as} \quad \frac{5.45 \text{ francs}}{1 \text{ dollar}}$$

To exchange a $50 bill for francs, you set up the ratio (fraction) so that dollars cancel, leaving you with francs. How many francs will you receive? Which fraction will you use? If you feel shaky on this decision, first estimate the answer. If you got 5 francs for each dollar, then you would get 250 francs for $50. You must have used the second fraction:

$$\frac{5.45 \text{ francs}}{1 \text{ dollar}} \times 50 \text{ dollars} = 272.5 \text{ francs}$$

If you want to convert 15,600 feet to miles, you can use the fact that there are 5,280 feet per mile; consequently:

$$15,600 \text{ feet} \times \frac{1 \text{ mile}}{5280 \text{ feet}} = 2.95 \text{ mile.}$$

Notice that the units "feet" cancel since $\frac{\text{feet}}{\text{feet}} = 1$.

Similarly, if you wish to change 0.62 mile to feet:

$$0.62 \text{ mile} \times \frac{5280 \text{ feet}}{1.0 \text{ mile}} = 3,274 \text{ feet.}$$

Depending on what you need to convert, you can use 1 mile/5280 feet or 5280 feet/1 mile). Your students will find this method very useful. The method can be used in any situation where unit conversion is needed. As another example, suppose you want to convert 3,400,000 inches to miles. You simply arrange the fractions so that inches cancel:

$$3,400,000 \text{ inches} \times \frac{1.0 \text{ foot}}{12 \text{ inches}} \times \frac{1 \text{ mile}}{5280 \text{ feet}} = 53.7 \text{ miles.}$$

Current rates of exchange for many countries can be found in the newspaper, at your local bank, or on the Internet. You might ask student teams to design some problems of their own using current exchange rates. You could then collect these problems and give them to other student teams to solve (or perhaps edit if they find errors in the problems).

Answers

1. a. $1000 × 100 yen/dollar = ¥100,000

    b. 1% of ¥100,000 = ¥1000; ¥100,000 − ¥1,000 = ¥99,000

2. ¥900 × 1 dollar/¥100) = $9; 1% of $9 = $0.09, leaving $8.91

3. $50 × 1 peso/$0.30 = 167 pesos

4. a. A total of L600,000 is required: (3 × L100,000) + (4 × L50,000) + (L100,000) = L600,000

    b. L600,000 × $1/L1505 = $399. You will need to exchange four $100 traveler's checks, assuming there is no fee for the transaction

5. a. L25,000 × $1/L1505 × F5/$1 = 83 francs

    b. L1505 = $1 = F5, so L1505 = F5 or L301 to the franc

9. *Speed, Time, and Distance*

(page 26)

Most real problems have units. This is just as true of problems that deal with distance, time, and speed as it is of problems involving the exchange of currencies. Continue to emphasize how essential it is to write in the units when solving most problems. For example, the first problem of this section should be written out as follows:

$$\frac{220 \text{ miles}}{4.0 \text{ hour}} = 55 \text{ miles/hour.}$$

In the second problem it is necessary to change 39 minutes to hours:

39 minutes × 1 hour/60 minutes = 0.65 hour. Notice that minutes/minutes = 1.

In the answers below, each problem is solved with all of the units in place.

Answers

1. 220 miles/4.0 hour = 55 miles/hour

2. 318 mi/2.65 hr = 120 mi/hr

3. 227 mi /120 mi/hr = 1.89 hours or 1 hour and 53.4 minutes

4. 520 mi/hr × 4.75 hr = 2470 miles

5. 280 mi/3 hr = 93 mi/hr

6. 50 mi/hr x 1.33 hr = 67 miles

7. 393 mi/5.2 hr = 76 mi/hr, well over the posted 65 mi/hr limit

8. $\frac{393}{60} = 6.55 \text{ hr} = 6 \text{ hr } 33 \text{ minutes}$

9. The driving time is 7.1 hours: 393 mi/ 55 mi/hr. Adding one hour for rest gives a total of 8.1 hours or 8 hours and 6 minutes.

10. Traveling on Nebraska 2 all the way should take 274 mi/45 mi/hr = 6.1 hours, or 6 hours and 6 minutes. The section on US 80 will take 265 mi/ 65 mi/hr = 4.1 hours. Traveling on Nebraska 385 will take 82 mi/55 mi/hr = 1.5 hours. This is a total travel time of 5.6 hours or 5 hours and 36 minutes, a half hour less than the travel time on Nebraska 2.

10. Time Zones in the United States *(page 29)*

Be sure to emphasize the irregularity of the actual time zones due to local needs and the underlying principle on which they are based.

In the spring we move all clocks forward an hour for Daylight Savings Time, DST, and in the fall we set the clocks back again to standard time. "Spring forward, fall back."

Answers

1. When it is 9 a.m., EST, in New York it is 6 a.m., PST, in Los Angeles.

2. When it is noon in Seattle it is 3 p.m. in Miami.

3. When it is 3 p.m. in LA it is 6 p.m. in NY. The flight left at noon from NY, so it took 6 hours.

4. a. In San Francisco it is 8 a.m. In Boston it is 11 a.m. DST. Seven hours later in Boston it will be 6 p.m. DST.

   b. If Boston is on EST, the clocks will read one hour earlier than they would if on daylight-saving time. Therefore, the clocks in Boston will read 5 p.m.

11. Shortest Travel Distances Along the Earth *(page 31)*

You will need a globe and a length of string for each student group. The shortest distance between two points is a straight line. However, we live on the surface of a sphere, where the shortest distance between two points is the arc that makes up part of a great circle whose plane passes through the earth's center. People, both old and young alike, tend to think that moving east or west is the shortest path between two points at the same lati-tude, but that is not true. The activity in this section makes it clear that the shortest path between two points on the globe is the arc of a circle that is a great circle.

A great circle is defined as the intersection of a plane passing through the center of a sphere and the sphere itself. It can be hard for students to grasp the concept of a great circle—that the plane of the circle can be at any angle, so long as the center of the earth is one point on the plane. You can demonstrate this by cutting an orange or other spherical object. You can slice through it at any angle, but as long as the knife passes through the center of the orange, all the cuts will have the same circumference. In the study of spherical geometry, it is proven that the shortest distance between any two points on a sphere lies on the great circle connecting the two points.

Students can see that this is true by actually measuring the distance between two points on a globe with a piece of string. Lines of latitude on a globe, other than the equator, do *not* form planes passing through the center of the sphere. Longitude lines, however, which all pass through the north and south poles, *do* form planes that pass through the earth's center. The easiest way to demonstrate the shortest distance theorem to your class is to choose two points at the same longitude but different latitudes.

For example, you can choose New York and Chala, Peru, which is south of Lima. Measure the distance between these cities along their common longitude. Now choose any other path (for example, via Mexico City), and do the same thing. The distance along the longitude, or great circle, will be the shortest.

In addition to learning a fundamental math principle, students will also learn some geography at no extra cost.

Answers

1. a. Across northern Canada and Alaska near the Arctic Circle; approximately 6800 miles as measured with string on the globe

   b. No.

2. a. Across Alaska and Siberia; approximately 8000 miles

   b. Over Greenland on a path that crosses the Arctic Circle twice; approximately 5000 miles

   c. Across western Canada, southern Alaska, the Bering Sea, eastern Russia, and eastern China; approximately 8500 miles

   d. No.

3. The Equator (0° latitude) is the only latitude line that is a great circle. The planes of the circles formed by all other lines of latitude lie north or south of the Earth's center.

4. a. $2606 + 2407 + 3940 = 8953$ miles

   b. It is more than 2100 miles longer than the great circle route.

5. a. 5965 miles

   b. Approx. 5500 miles

   c. $465/5965 \times 100 = 7.8\%$ fuel or time saving

6. a. The total distance from London, England to Wellington, New Zealand via New York is $3500 + 9067 = 12{,}567$ miles. This is $12567 - 11790 = 777$ miles longer than the direct route.

   b. Flying at a steady velocity, this 777 miles represents a saving in fuel of $777/12567 \times 100 = 6.2\%$.

   c. A great circle route

12. Weather Maps *(page 34)*

Learning to read and interpret a map is an important mathematical skill. Weather maps are especially complicated because they contain so much symbolism peculiar to them. It would be a good idea to spend some time going over this symbolism with your students before they begin working on the problems.

Answers

1. The temperature in Chicago was in the 60's; actually 66° F according to a listing.

2. The map shows a region in the 30's just north of Fargo, North Dakota and into northern Minnesota.

3. South of Phoenix, Arizona the temperatures were in the 100's, the warmest area in the country. Phoenix itself just reached 100° F.

4. Just south of New York there is a warm front moving north. It should turn warmer in the immediate future, with the possibility of rain moving in from the west.

5. Just north of Dallas there is a cold front moving south. The weather should turn colder but continue clear.

6. A cold front has just passed over Chicago so yesterday was probably warmer than today. It should have been in the 70's yesterday and it is in the 60's today. (Actually, at 2 p.m. it was 68°F yesterday and 66°F today. The prediction for tomorrow is 46°F with clouds moving in from the north.)

13. Road Maps *(page 36)*

Students will need a road map, a ruler, and a cloth measuring tape for these activities.

Everyone travels, often by car, and the distance to be traveled can be determined in advance by consulting a road map. This activity will give students experience with maps and scaling. It will also make them realize that maps are useful in planning a trip as well as a device to avoid becoming lost.

Students could be asked to bring road maps from home, or your local chamber of commerce might provide maps of your town or city. If the distances that students measure on their maps are significant, you might extend the activity by asking such questions as:

How fast do you think you would travel along the road(s) connecting the two towns? (Maps usually indicate the type of road as well as its path.)

How long would it take to travel between the two towns?

If you are driving a car that gets 40 km/gal (25 mpg), how much gasoline would be needed to make the trip?

14. Measuring Distance with a Wheel *(page 38)*

This section describes how a trundle wheel is used to measure distance. Students can substitute their own bicycle wheels to measure distances. Be sure to emphasize safety if students do these activities. They should not try to ride their bikes and count turns of the wheel simultaneously. They should work with a partner who will keep an eye out for traffic, pedestrians, and other cyclists.

Answers

1. a. 1,000 m ÷ 2.07 m/turn = 483 turns
    b. 5,280 ft. ÷ 6.8 ft./turn = 776 turns
    c. 776 turns/mi. ÷ 483 turns/km = 1.61 km/mi

2. a. Answers will vary depending on the bike.

b. $2\pi \times$ measured radius

c. (1) Answers will vary.

(2) Answers will vary.

(3) 360 feet if it is a regulation diamond; 240 feet if softball or little league field.

(4) A football field from goal line to goal line is 300 ft. × 150 ft. = 45,000 sq. ft. or 5,000 sq. yd. If the end zones are included, another 20 yd. × 50 yd. = 1,000 sq. yd. or 9,000 sq. ft should be added. Soccer fields vary in length from 100 to 130 m and in width from 45 m to 90 m; consequently answers may vary from 5,000 sq. m to 11,700 sq. m.

15. MPG *(page 40)*

In the United States, the primary means of travel is by automobile. Students generally look forward to the day when they will have a license to drive and own a car. But an automobile is an expensive piece of equipment to both own and operate. This section focuses on fuel economy—the number of miles a car will travel on a gallon of gasoline, which can be calculated using data that is easy to collect.

Answers

1. a. (11739.4 - 11432.0) mi = 307.4 miles
    b. Divide distance (miles) traveled by fuel used (gallons). In this case 307.4 mi ÷ 10.6 gal = 29 mpg.
2. a. (12765.0 – 11952.7) mi = 812.3 miles
    b. 812.3 mi. ÷ (11.3 + 9.8) gal. = 38.5 mpg
    c. Fuel economy is better for highway driving than city driving, which requires many stops and driving in lower gear ratios.

8. Change, Cambio, Wechsel: Changing Foreign Currency

Change, Cambio, Wechsel—you'll see these signs all over Europe. They alert travelers to the fact that they need a different currency to pay for goods. If you are one of those travelers and have a pocket calculator, you can easily figure out how much your dollars are worth in the currency of the country you are visiting. And on your way home you can figure out how many dollars you should receive for the foreign currency you have in your wallet or purse.

Suppose the sign in the Paris exchange window indicates that U.S. traveler's checks can be exchanged at F5.00 for a dollar. (F is for French francs.) This can be written as:

$$\frac{1 \text{ dollar}}{5 \text{ francs}} \text{ or as } \frac{5 \text{ francs}}{1 \text{ dollar}}$$

You would like to exchange a $50 traveler's check. How many francs will you receive? Which fraction will you use? If you are uncertain, estimate the answer first. If you got 5 francs for each dollar, then you would get 250 francs for $50. You must have used the second fraction:

$$\frac{5 \text{ francs}}{1 \text{ dollar}} \times 50 \text{ dollars} = 250 \text{ francs}$$

Think of the word "dollar" as canceling. This is the same idea as:

$$\frac{7}{3} \times 3 = 7$$

The 3's cancel because $3 \div 3 = 1$. That is why we drew a line through the 3's. The same can be done with dollars because $\frac{\text{dollar}}{\text{dollar}} = 1$.

Suppose you see a sweater in a Parisian shop with a price tag that reads F450. Is this a good buy? You will want to convert F450 to dollars to get an idea of the price in a familiar currency. You want francs to cancel, so you multiply:

$$\frac{1 \text{ dollar}}{5 \text{ francs}} \times 450 \text{ francs} = \$90.$$

Now you can decide whether the price is a good one.

The following problems contain some real-life money situations that you might meet when traveling in other countries.

(continued)

8. Change, Cambio, Wechsel: Changing Foreign Currency

(continued)

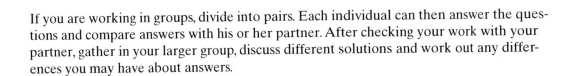

If you are working in groups, divide into pairs. Each individual can then answer the questions and compare answers with his or her partner. After checking your work with your partner, gather in your larger group, discuss different solutions and work out any differences you may have about answers.

1. You have just arrived in Japan, at Narita Airport. Japanese yen are exchanging at 100 yen to the dollar. How many yen (¥) can you expect to receive for a $1000 traveler's check if:

   a. there is no fee for exchanging currency? _____

   b. a 1% fee is charged for such an exchange? _____

2. When leaving Narita Airport for the United States, you have 900 yen to change back to dollars. There is a 1% fee for making the exchange. How much can you expect to receive in dollars?

   _____

3. In Mexico City, a sign in a bank window states that the peso is exchanging at $0.30 per peso. How many pesos will you receive for a $50 traveler's check?

   _____

4. You are planning to spend four days (three nights) in Italy. The exchange rate is L1505 to the dollar. You will be staying at a hotel in Florence. It would be easiest for you to pick up Italian lira (L) when you arrive at the train station in the city. You know that your room will cost L100,000 per night, and you estimate that food will cost L50,000 per day. You estimate that you will spend another L100,000 for expenses (museums, taxis, souvenirs, etc.).

   a. How much Italian money do you expect to spend during your visit to Italy?

   _____

   b. How many $100 traveler's checks should you exchange at the station to meet your need for lira? _____

5. Leaving Italy for France, you find that you still have L25,000.

   a. How many French francs will you receive at the rates of exchange quoted above?

   _____

   b. What is the exchange rate of lira to the franc? _____

9. Speed, Time, and Distance

You're in the family car, taking a trip to see cousins who live a long distance away. You have already asked the driver more than once, "How long before we get there?"

A road sign you just passed indicates your destination is still 250 miles away. Your mother, who is driving, tells you that she expects to average 50 miles per hour for the rest of the trip. If she maintains the speed she expects to, the rest of the trip should take five hours. A speed of 50 miles per hour means you should travel 50 miles every hour. If that steady speed is maintained, you should go 250 miles in five hours because:

$$50 \, \frac{\text{miles}}{\cancel{\text{hour}}} \times 5 \, \cancel{\text{hour}} = 250 \text{ miles}$$

What if the sign had said 265 miles, and your average speed was 55 miles per hour? The approximate travel time would still be about five hours.

Suppose we wanted a more exact time. We have previously found that

$$50 \, \frac{\text{miles}}{\cancel{\text{hour}}} \times 5 \, \cancel{\text{hour}} = 250 \text{ miles}$$

In fact, any speed, or **velocity**, multiplied by time will give a distance. We can say that:

$$\text{velocity} \times \text{time} = \text{distance}$$

We can divide both sides of this equation by velocity. After all, if we divide equals by equals, we should still have equals. So we have:

$$\frac{\cancel{\text{velocity}} \times \text{time}}{\cancel{\text{velocity}}} = \frac{\text{distance}}{\text{velocity}}$$

or

$$\text{time} = \frac{\text{distance}}{\text{velocity}}$$

If we look at the units in this simple expression, we see that we might have:

$$\text{hours} = \frac{\text{miles}}{\frac{\text{miles}}{\text{hour}}}$$

When we divide by a fraction we must invert and multiply. For example:

$$\frac{2}{\frac{1}{2}} = 2 \times \frac{2}{1} = 4$$

(continued)

Middle School Math You Really Need

Name _____   Date _____

9. Speed, Time, and Distance *(continued)*

So our units equation could be written as:

$$\text{hours} = \cancel{\text{miles}} \times \frac{\text{hour}}{\cancel{\text{miles}}} = \text{hours}$$

This makes sense because hours must equal hours. We certainly can't say that hours = miles. A time can't equal a distance.

Returning to our question about the time required to travel 265 miles at 55 miles per hour, we can write:

$$\text{time} = \frac{\text{distance}}{\text{velocity}} = \frac{265 \text{ miles}}{55 \dfrac{\text{miles}}{\text{hour}}} = 4.8 \text{ hours}$$

If you want to know the time in hours and minutes, you can easily change 0.8 hour to minutes. Because there are 60 minutes in one hour:

$$0.8 \cancel{\text{hour}} \times \frac{60 \text{ minutes}}{1.0 \text{ hour}} = 48 \text{ minutes}$$

So the total time for the trip will be 4 hours and 48 minutes. Including units in your calculations will certainly give you a lot more confidence in knowing that your answer is at least a reasonable one.

Using what you have learned about the relationships among speed, distance, and time, work on the following problems that might be encountered by a traveler.

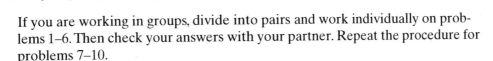

If you are working in groups, divide into pairs and work individually on problems 1–6. Then check your answers with your partner. Repeat the procedure for problems 7–10.

After completing all 10 problems go back into your larger group, discuss different solutions, and work out any disagreements you may have about answers.

▼ ▼ ▼ ▼ ▼ ▼ ▼ ▼ ▼ ▼ ▼ ▼ ▼ ▼ ▼ ▼ ▼ ▼

1. What is the average speed of a car that goes 220 miles in 4.0 hours?

   _____

2. The Tokyo to Kyoto "bullet train," the Shinkansen Express, travels the 318-mile distance between the two cities in exactly 2 hours and 39 minutes. It is very regular. You can almost always set your watch by your arrival time. What is the average speed of this train? (You can add the 39 minutes to the 2 hours by first dividing 39 minutes by 60, since there are 60 minutes in an hour. This will give you the total time in hours as 2 + a decimal fraction.)

(continued)

9. Speed, Time, and Distance *(continued)*

3. Maintaining this same average speed, how long should the bullet train take to reach Nagoya, a city 227 miles from Tokyo? _____

4. Just after leaving New York, the pilot of your 747 jet announces that the plane will be traveling at a steady speed of 520 mi/hr. It is scheduled to arrive in Los Angeles in 4 hours and 45 minutes. How far will you travel on this New York to Los Angeles flight? _____

5. What is the average speed of a train that travels 280 miles in 3.0 hours?

_____

6. How far will a car travel if it maintains a steady speed of 50 mi/hr for an hour and 20 minutes? _____

7. You can drive all of the way from Buffalo to New York City on US 90 and 87, a distance of 393 miles. You need to be in New York City in 5.2 hours. What average speed must you maintain? Can you make this trip in the time given without breaking the speed limit of 65 mph? _____

_____

8. If you can average 60 mph, how long will it take you to drive from Buffalo to New York City? _____

9. How long will it take to travel from Buffalo to New York City if you average 55 mi/hr while driving and stop for a one hour rest? _____

10. In Nebraska there are several ways to go from Grand Island to Alliance. You can travel on Nebraska 2 all the way, a distance of 274 miles, with an average speed of 45 mi/hr. Or, for the first 265 miles, you can travel on US 80, an interstate highway that allows you to maintain an average speed of 65 mi/hr. But US 80 takes you only part of the way. Leaving US 80, you must travel on Nebraska 385 for 82 more miles to reach Alliance. On Nebraska 385 you can maintain an average speed of 55 mi/hr. Which route will take the least time? _____

10. Time Zones in the United States

The distance around the world (its circumference) is approximately 24,000 miles at the equator. There are 24 hours in a day, and 360° in a circle—like the Equator. If we divide the Equator into 24 equal parts, each part will take up 15° (360° ÷ 24 = 15°). These 24 areas are called **time zones**. Because 24,000 ÷ 24 = 1000, each time zone is 1000 miles wide at the Equator. As we move north or south from the Equator, each time zone becomes narrower, as shown in Figure 2.1. However, each zone is still 15° wide. As you can see from Figure 2.1, the distance around lines of latitude becomes smaller as we move toward the North or South Pole along lines of longitude.

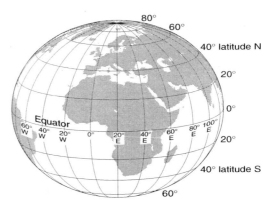

Figure 2.1. Lines of latitude circle the earth. They are parallel to the Equator which is 0° latitude. Lines of longitude run from the North Pole (90° north latitude) to the South Pole (90° south latitude).

Lines of latitude across the United States are from approximately 25° to 50°. The lines of longitude range from about 70° to 125°—a total of about 55° in the east-west direction. If we divide 55° by 15° we get about 3⅔ time zones across the United States. The average width of the United States is approximately 2800 miles.

As a result, the country is divided into four time zones—Eastern, Central, Mountain, and Pacific. These are abbreviated as EST, CST, MST, and PST for Eastern Standard Time, Central Standard Time, etc. As you can see from Figure 2.2, the boundaries of these time zones do not always lie along lines of longitude. This is because political and social factors enter into deciding on time zones.

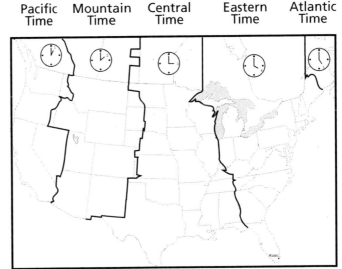

Figure 2.2. The continental United States has four major time zones.

(continued)

         Middle School Math You Really Need

10. Time Zones in the United States *(continued)*

During the summer months, many states change to daylight saving time—DST. This means that in the spring (usually in April), they move the time ahead one hour. In the fall (usually October), they resume standard time and turn their clocks back one hour.

Dividing the nation's average width, 2800 miles, into four zones gives an average width of only 700 miles for each zone. This is $\frac{7}{10}$ of the average width of a time zone at the equator. At the poles, the lines of longitude come together, and the width of each zone shrinks to zero.

Anyone traveling across the country or making phone calls to people in other time zones must take the difference in time into account. No one wants to be called after they have gone to sleep. The problems that follow will make you aware of how mathematics is used in taking time zones into account.

▼ ▼ ▼ ▼ ▼ ▼ ▼ ▼ ▼ ▼ ▼ ▼ ▼ ▼ ▼ ▼ ▼ ▼

If you are working in groups of four, have each member do one of the four problems. Then come back together and have each person explain to the other three how he or she did the problem assigned. Other members of the group can then agree with the solution, point out errors, or suggest other ways to do the problem.

▼ ▼ ▼ ▼ ▼ ▼ ▼ ▼ ▼ ▼ ▼ ▼ ▼ ▼ ▼ ▼ ▼ ▼

1. What time is it in Los Angeles when it is 9 a.m. (EST) in New York?

   _____

2. What time is it in Miami when it is noon (PST) in Seattle?

   _____

3. A non-stop plane leaves New York at noon (EST) headed for Los Angeles. What is its flight time if it arrives at its destination at 3 p.m. local standard time?

   _____

4. A non-stop plane leaves San Francisco for Boston at 8 a.m., daylight saving time. The flight time is 7 hours. What will the clocks in Boston read when the plane lands if:

   a. Boston is also on daylight saving time? _____

   b. Boston is on EST? _____

Middle School Math You Really Need

11. Shortest Travel Distances Along the Earth

▼ ▼ ▼ ▼ ▼ ▼ ▼ ▼ ▼ ▼ ▼ ▼ ▼ ▼ ▼ ▼ ▼ ▼

If you are working in groups of four, have one member use the string to measure distances on the globe while a second member holds the globe in place. Have a third person check the measurement before a fourth person records the data. Then solve all the problems together. Compare your results with those of another group.

▼ ▼ ▼ ▼ ▼ ▼ ▼ ▼ ▼ ▼ ▼ ▼ ▼ ▼ ▼ ▼ ▼ ▼

Airplanes flying nonstop from New York to Tokyo don't fly west along a line of latitude near 40° north. Instead, they fly north.

To find out why, wrap a strong string around a globe at the Equator. Measure the circumference of the globe at the Equator by placing the string on a ruler or yardstick. The distance around the real earth's Equator is 24,900 miles (40,000 kilometers). The circumference of your globe represents 24,900 miles on the real globe that we live on. You can use this to figure out the globe's scale in inches per mile. For example, if the distance around your globe is 38 inches, then each inch on the globe corresponds to 655 miles (24,900 mi ÷ 38 in = 655 mi/in). You can use the scale of your globe to find the shortest distance between cities around the world.

1. Use the same string to find the shortest distance from New York to Tokyo. You can do this by laying the string on the globe.

   a. What is the shortest path along the globe from New York to Tokyo? Approximately how long is it in miles? _____

   b. Does that shortest path lie close to the 40° latitude line? _____

2. What is the shortest route from:

   a. Los Angeles to New Delhi, India? Approximately how long is it?

   _____

   b. Chicago to Moscow, Russia? Approximately how long is it?

   _____

   c. New Orleans to Hong Kong? Approximately how long is it?

   _____

   d. Do any of these paths lie along lines of latitude? _____

After finding the shortest paths between distant points on a globe, you know that these paths are not usually along lines of latitude. If you measure shortest routes carefully, you will find that they lie along what are called *great circles*.

(continued)

11. Shortest Travel Distances Along the Earth *(continued)*

A great circle is formed by an imaginary plane that passes through the center of the earth and the earth's surface. The shortest distance between any two points on the surface of the globe lies on the great circle connecting the points. Any other path is longer. Figure 2.3 shows a great circle on the globe. The shortest distance between A and B lies on the great circle route, not on any other route. It is usually easy for airplanes to follow great-circle routes. Ocean-going ships, however, often have to deviate from great circle routes because of land barriers, icebergs, or unfavorable ocean currents.

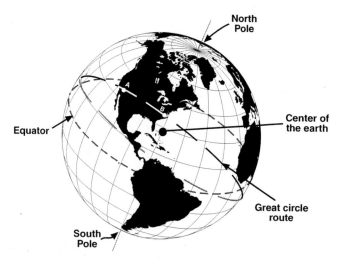

Figure 2.3. A great circle on the globe has a plane that passes through the earth's center. The equator (0° latitude) is the only latitude line that is a great circle. All lines of longitude are great circles. Why?

Since a great circle is any circle on the surface of the earth whose center is at the earth's center, all the lines of longitude are great circles. The lines that separate the sections of a peeled orange are very nearly great circles.

3. Which line of latitude is a great circle? _____

4. Here are some actual airline distances for a New York to Tokyo flight stopping in San Francisco and Honolulu:

New York to San Francisco	2606 miles
San Francisco to Honolulu	2407 miles
Honolulu to Tokyo	3940 miles

a. What is the total flight distance from New York to Tokyo?

_____

b. How does this compare with the great circle route you measured in problem 1?

(continued)

11. Shortest Travel Distances Along the Earth *(continued)*

5. The airline distances between Los Angeles and New York and between New York and London are given below:

   Los Angeles to New York   2465 miles

   New York to London   3500 miles

   a. What is the total flight distance from London to Los Angeles via New York?

   _____

   b. Using string, ruler, and globe, what is the shortest flight path from London to Los Angeles?

   _____

   c. What percentage of fuel and time would be saved by flying a great circle route between London and Los Angeles?

   _____

6. A traveler wants to fly directly from London, England to Wellington, the capital of New Zealand. He looks at a Mercator projection of the world and decides that London to New York and New York to Wellington would be the best route. London to New York is 3500 miles and New York to Wellington is 9067 miles, non-stop across the Pacific Ocean. But an airline schedule lists London to Wellington *direct* as 11790 miles.

   a. Compare these two routes for difference in mileage.

   London to New York to Wellington: _____

   London to Wellington direct: _____

   b. What percentage of fuel would be saved flying the shorter route when compared with the longer route? _____

   c. What route do you think the shorter flight follows? _____

   _____

12. Weather Maps

If you are traveling, one of the things you must consider is the weather. Most radio stations give frequent weather reports, and both television and newspapers provide detailed weather maps and reports. Figure 2.4 is the weather map for the United States at 2 p.m. EST, April 25, 1996. The alternating shaded and clear bands show areas of common temperature. The dark bands of triangles indicate the direction of motion of a cold front, a region of cold air moving toward the points of the shaded triangles. The shaded half circles show the direction of motion of a warm front. In the United States these fronts almost always move in an easterly direction.

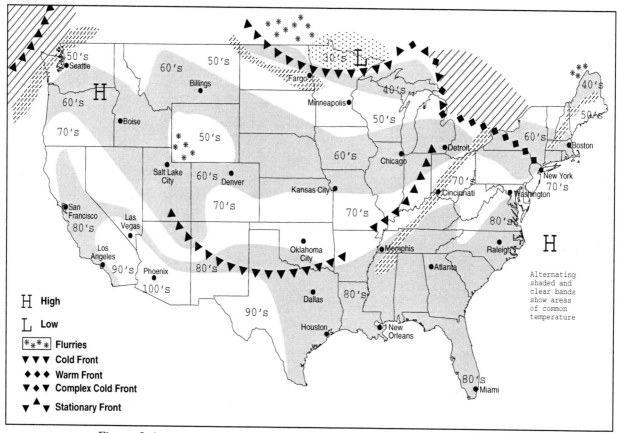

Figure 2.4. A weather map for April 25, 1996 @ 2 p.m. EDT

The letter "H" indicates a region of high pressure; the letter "L" indicates a region of low pressure. High pressure areas are usually associated with fair weather; low pressure areas are often associated with clouds and precipitation.

(continued)

12. Weather Maps *(continued)*

▼ ▼

If you are working in groups, each member of the group can be assigned one of the first four problems and then work on either question 5 or 6 or both until all members have completed at least two of the questions. The group can then reassemble. Each member can explain to the group how he or she arrived at the answer to each of the first four questions before questions 5 and 6 are discussed as a group. Try to reach agreement or reasons for any disagreements on answers to problems 5 and 6.

▼ ▼

1. What was the 2 p. m. temperature in Chicago? _____

2. Where was it the coldest in the U.S.? _____

3. Where was it the warmest in the U.S.? _____

4. What does the map predict will happen in the next day to the weather in New York? Why do you think so? _____

   _____

5. What does the map predict for the weather in the next day in Dallas?

   _____

6. Describe the weather in Chicago on April 24, and predict the weather there for April 26.

   _____

   _____

   _____

13. Road Maps

If you are traveling by car, road maps are very helpful. When traveling in an unfamiliar area, they are essential. Look closely at a road map or road atlas. You will find a scale that shows the length in centimeters or inches of a kilometer or mile on the map. Depending on the map's size, detail, and the area it covers, a centimeter may equal a kilometer, 10 kilometers, $\frac{1}{10}$ kilometer, or some other value.

With the map, a ruler, a cloth measuring tape, pencil, and paper, you can find distances between your towns on the map. Use the ruler to measure along straight roads connecting points on the map or to find "as the crow flies" measurements between points on the map. Use the flexible cloth tape to measure roads that curve.

From the measurements and the scale on the map, you can determine the distances between points on the map. For example, you might find that there are 4.0 centimeters of road between towns A and B on a map. The map's scale indicates 20 km for every 3.1 cm on the map. You determine the distance between towns A and B by calculation or by drawing an extended map scale on a sheet of paper. Calculation shows that there are:

$$\frac{20 \text{ km}}{3.1 \text{ cm}} = 6.5 \text{ km/cm}.$$

Therefore, the distance between A and B is:

$$4.0 \text{ cm} \times 6.5 \text{ km/cm} = 26 \text{ km}.$$

Figure 2.5 shows how you can extend the scale shown on the map. You then simply find where 4.0 cm lies along that scale to find the distance between towns A and B.

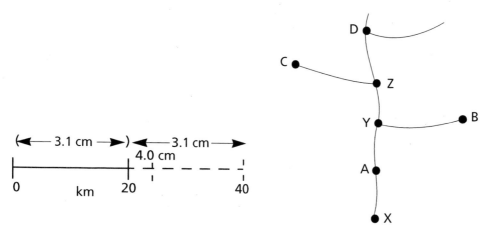

Figure 2.5. Dotted lines show the map scale extended. If distance on a map is 4.0 cm as shown, then the distance represented by 4.0 cm is 4.0 cm times the scale factor. In this case, the scale factor is 6.5 km/cm. Therefore, 4.0 cm × 6.5 km/cm = 26 km.

(continued)

13. Road Maps *(continued)*

▼ ▼ ▼ ▼ ▼ ▼ ▼ ▼ ▼ ▼ ▼ ▼ ▼ ▼ ▼ ▼ ▼ ▼ ▼ ▼

It's probably best to do this map work in pairs. Each pair will need a road map, ruler, cloth measuring tape, paper, and pencil. Determine two points on the map whose driving distance and "as the crow flies" distances you wish to measure. One person can then do the measuring while the other records the numbers. Then you can work together to determine the distance either by calculation or by extending the map's scale. Repeat the process for a number of different points on the map.

Some maps give information about the distances between major cities. You can check up on your technique by comparing your measurements of distance with those provided on the map.

▼ ▼ ▼ ▼ ▼ ▼ ▼ ▼ ▼ ▼ ▼ ▼ ▼ ▼ ▼ ▼ ▼ ▼ ▼ ▼

Point A name: _____

Point B name: _____

Actual map measurements A to B (in cm)

"As the crow flies": _____

By road: _____

Distance in miles A to B

"As the crow flies": _____

By road: _____

14. Measuring Distance with a Wheel

The distances you find on road maps were measured before the map was drawn. One way to measure distances is to use a trundle wheel. You may have seen highway surveyors rolling a small wheel like the one shown in Figure 2.6. The surveyor counts the number of turns the wheel makes when it is rolled from one point to another. Knowing the diameter or radius of the wheel and the number of turns it made as it was rolled, the distance between the two points can be calculated.

You can do the same thing with your bicycle. Measure the diameter of the bike's wheel with a yardstick or a meter stick as shown in Figure 2.7. Suppose the wheel's diameter is 66 cm (0.66 m), or 26 inches. When the wheel makes one turn, it will roll a distance equal to the wheel's circumference (the distance around the outside of the wheel).

This distance is equal to π times the diameter (or 2π times the radius) of the wheel. As you may know, π (pronounced pi) shows the relationship between the diameter and the circumference of a circle. It is equal to the circumference of a circle divided by its diameter or by twice its radius. No matter what the size of the circle is, the diameter will always divide into the circumference the same number of times. The value of π is always the same. It is a never-ending decimal with a value of 3.1416 . . . . As a reasonable approximation, you can use 3.14 for π. If the wheel's radius is 33 cm (13 inches), then the distance it rolls with each turn is approximately:

$2\pi \times 33$ cm $= 2 \times 3.14 \times 33$ cm $= 207$ cm

or 2.07 m (81.6 in or 6.8 ft)

If the bike wheel rolls through 10 complete turns, it has traveled 20.7 m (68 ft.).

1 Turn of wheel

Figure 2.6. A trundle wheel can be used to measure distance. Each turn of the wheel measures a distance equal to the wheel's circumference.

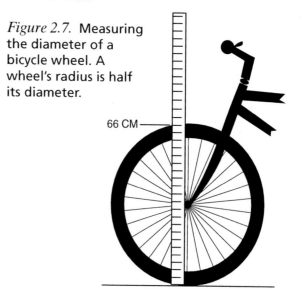

Figure 2.7. Measuring the diameter of a bicycle wheel. A wheel's radius is half its diameter.

66 CM

(continued)

14. Measuring Distance with a Wheel *(continued)*

▼ ▼ ▼ ▼ ▼ ▼ ▼ ▼ ▼ ▼ ▼ ▼ ▼ ▼ ▼ ▼ ▼ ▼

This work should be done in pairs. The first question can be answered with your partner. Then check your answer with another pair of students. Your teacher will probably want to discuss question 2 with you before you begin working on it. You and your partner can take turns rolling the wheel. The second person should act as an observer and make sure the measurement is done safely. Follow all safety instructions carefully.

▼ ▼ ▼ ▼ ▼ ▼ ▼ ▼ ▼ ▼ ▼ ▼ ▼ ▼ ▼ ▼ ▼ ▼

1. How many turns of the wheel are needed for the 66 cm (26") wheel described above to travel:

   a. 1.0 kilometer (km)? _____

   b. 1.0 mile? _____

   c. Use the answers to parts a. and b. to find the number of kilometers in one mile.

2. Use your own bicycle wheel to measure distances. Place a piece of tape on the rim to serve as a marker. The marker will allow you to count the number of turns easily. Walk beside the bicycle as you roll it along count-ing the number of times the wheel turns. Have someone walk beside you to prevent you from bumping into people or objects. **Do not try to ride the bike while counting turns!** It would be dangerous to do so.

   a. What is the radius of your bicycle wheel? _____

   b. How far does the wheel go each time it goes around? _____

   c. Use your bicycle wheel to measure:

      (1) the length of your street or block: _____

      (2) the distance to your school (if within walking distance):

      _____

      (3) the distance around the base paths of a baseball field:

      _____

      (4) the area within the lines of a football or soccer field:

      _____

15. MPG

One of the things a car owner or buyer wants to know is how far the car will go on one gallon of gasoline. This is commonly called miles per gallon, or just mpg.

To find mpg it is not necessary to drain the gasoline tank, add exactly one gallon of fuel, and then drive until the car stops. The easiest way is to fill the tank and record the reading on the odometer. The odometer measures the distance that the car has traveled in miles or in kilometers. When the needle on the fuel gauge approaches zero, fill the tank again. This time record both the odometer reading and the number of gallons needed to fill the tank. This is all the information needed to find the car's mpg.

▼ ▼ ▼ ▼ ▼ ▼ ▼ ▼ ▼ ▼ ▼ ▼ ▼ ▼ ▼ ▼ ▼ ▼

Answer the four questions that follow individually. Then check your answers with your partner. Finally gather in a larger group to discuss any differences in solutions and answers.

▼ ▼ ▼ ▼ ▼ ▼ ▼ ▼ ▼ ▼ ▼ ▼ ▼ ▼ ▼ ▼ ▼ ▼

1. A driver fills her gasoline tank and records the reading on the odometer. It is 11432.0 (miles). A week later, she fills the tank again. It takes 10.6 gallons to fill the tank. The odometer now reads 11739.4 (miles).

   a. How far did the car travel during the week between fuelings? _____

   b. How can the driver calculate the distance her car travels on one gallon of gasoline?

   _____

2. The driver realizes that most of her driving during the week consisted of short trips within her town. She wonders if the car's mpg would improve if she took a long trip on a highway.

   The following weekend she again fills the car's tank with fuel and records the odometer reading. It is 11952.7. She then drives five hours to visit her grandmother. After the weekend, she returns by the same route. During the return trip, she fills the tank again. It takes 11.3 gallons to fill the tank. After reaching home, she fills the tank once more. This time 9.8 gallons are needed and the odometer reads 12765.0.

   a. How far did she travel during this weekend trip? _____

   b. What was her car's mpg for this trip? _____

   c. What can the driver conclude about fuel economy (mpg) for highway driving compared to in-city driving? _____

40   *Middle School Math You Really Need*

CHAPTER 3 Math and Sports

To the Teacher

16. What's My Fielding Percentage? *(page 46)*

The game of baseball generates a myriad of statistics. Many of these statistics are used comparatively and fuel arguments about whether player A or B is "better." This activity can be augmented during the baseball season by using actual current statistics from a weekend's games or a student's personal performance on a little league or school team. Students can also be asked to keep track of a favorite player or to predict changes in the statistics of these players based upon a one or two game performance.

Answers

1. Answers will vary. Willie Mays' fielding percentage was .977.

2. Clemente's fielding percentage was .986.

3. Robinson's fielding percentage was .968.

4. Answers will vary. The students may conclude that third base is a more difficult position defensively than right field.

5. Campanella's fielding percentage was .988, and Bench's fielding percentage was .990. Bench played more games (due to Campanella's tragic automobile accident that paralyzed him), and had a better fielding percentage.

6. Cuyler's fielding percentage was .972.

7. Rodriguez's fielding percentage was .977.

8. Griffey's fielding percentage was .990.

9. The Cub's Team fielding percentage was .983.

10. Cobb's fielding percentage was .961.

17. What's My Earned Run Average? *(page 49)*

Answers

1. Because it is not possible to catch more balls than come to you, or to drop more than you have the opportunity to field, fielding percentages must be between 0.000 and 1.000. Not so with earned run averages. ERAs are comparative statistics between earned runs yielded and innings pitched, and the one does not limit the other. Consequently, although ERAs cannot go below 0.00, they can go up to "infinity" or "undefined." The lowest one season ERA in history (pitchers with 100 or more innings) was Dutch Leonard's 1.01 in 1914. The highest ERA of "infinity" is shared by Louis Walter "Kid" Bauer and others.

2. Cicotte's career ERA was 2.37.

3. Marberry's career ERA was 3.63.

4. Newhouser's combined ERA for 1944 and 1945 was 2.02.

5. Koufax's career ERA was 2.76 and Gibson's was 2.91. Koufax's is lower, but Gibson pitched farther into the twilight of his career.

6. Bauer's ERA was "infinity" or "undefined," because it was $2 \div 0$.

18. In the Sports Pages *(page 51)*

Some students are motivated to read because of their interest in the sports pages of the newspaper, where reports of their favorite teams and players are to be found. But there are numbers as well as words on the sports pages, and the next several sections use information found in the sports pages to illustrate additional uses of mathematics in sports.

Answers

1. a. $\frac{3}{3} = 1.0 = 100\%$

    b. $\frac{2}{3} = 0.67 = 67\%$

    c. $\frac{1}{3} = 0.33 = 33\%$

    d. $\frac{0}{3} = 0 = 0\%$

2. a. Hamilton

    b. Montreal.

    c. Hamilton scored 96 points in 3 games—an average of 32 points per game—the highest of any team in the standings.

      Montreal had allowed only 50 points in 3 games—an average of 16.7 points per game—the least of any team in the league.

3. a. 2

    b. 1

    c. 0

4. 96 points /3 games = 32 points/game

5. 50 points/3 games = 16.7 points/ game

6. Yes. Yes. Any points scored by a team will appear in the points scored against column for other teams and vice versa.

19. More in the Sports Pages
(page 53)

This section provides another example of how math is used in the sports section of a newspaper.

Answers

East	W	L	Pct.	GB
New York	52	33	.612	—
Baltimore	46	39	.541	6
Toronto	38	49	.437	15
Boston	36	49	.424	16
Detroit	27	61	.307	26.5
Central	**W**	**L**	**Pct.**	**GB**
Cleveland	52	35	.598	—
Chicago	50	37	.575	2
Milwaukee	43	43	.500	$8\frac{1}{2}$
Minnesota	41	45	.477	$10\frac{1}{2}$
West	**W**	**L**	**Pct.**	**GB**
Texas	51	36	.586	—
Seattle	46	39	.541	4
California	43	45	.489	$4\frac{1}{2}$
Oakland	43	45	.489	0

20. Still More from the Sports Pages *(page 55)*

Although the math used here may be of more interest to team owners than to players, it provides information that is useful in determining how well fans in different cities support their professional baseball teams.

Answers

1. Yes (or at least they should).

2., 3.

Team	Dates	Attend.	Avg. attend.
Baltimore	46	2,038,534	44,316
Boston	41	1,133,451	27,645
California	44	1,054,715	23,971
Chicago	40	843,836	21,096
Cleveland	44	1,839,190	41,800
Detroit	43	638,789	14,856
Kansas City	43	781,556	18,176
Milwaukee	40	585,510	14,638
Minnesota	44	766,877	17,429
New York	45	1,119,291	24,873
Oakland	41	516,942	12,608
Seattle	44	1,455,177	33,072
Texas	46	1,610,768	35,017
Toronto	41	1,289,964	31,463
A.L Totals	602	15,674,600	26,038
N.L. Totals	601	16,009,881	26,639

4. The total dates for the two leagues differ by only one game. The average attendance figures are also very similar. They differ by only 601. The National League's average attendance is about 2.3% higher than that of the American League.

21. *Math at the Olympics* (page 57)

The Olympic Games enjoy world-wide interest among people of all ages. The questions that follow illustrate how mathematics can be applied to events that take place at the Olympics.

Students may enjoy devising questions of their own that are related to the Olympic Games. Almanaces are a good source for statistics to use in preparing questions. These questions can then be shared with other groups or individuals in your class.

Answers

1. a. 100.00 m/9.84 s = 10.16 m/s.

   b. 100 $\cancel{m}$ × 3.28 ft/$\cancel{m}$ = 328 ft; 328 ft/ 9.84 s = 33.3 ft/s

   c. $\dfrac{33.3 \cancel{ft}}{1.00 \cancel{s}} \times \dfrac{1.00 \text{ mi}}{5280 \cancel{ft}} \times \dfrac{3600 \cancel{s}}{1.00 \text{ h}}$ = 22.7 mph

   d. 100.00 m/12.0 s = 8.33 m/s

   e. 10.2/8.33 = 1.22

   f. 22.7 mph/1.22 = 18.6 mph

2. a. 200 m/19.32 s = 10.35 m/s

   b. 10.35 $\cancel{m/s}$ × 3.28 $\cancel{ft/m}$ × 1 mi/5280 $\cancel{ft}$ × 3600 $\cancel{s}$/h = 23.1 mph

   c. 200 m/22.2 s = 9.01 m/s

   d. 10.35/9.01 = 1.15

   e. 22.2/19.32 = 1.15. The result is the same. Perhaps students will see that for the same distance, velocity, and time are related in an inverse way.

3. a.

Distance (m)	Speed (m/s)
100	10.16
200	10.35
400	9.24
800	7.86
1000	7.57
1500	7.23
2000	6.95
5000	6.54
10,000	6.24
20,000	5.86
25,000	5.64
Marathon	5.56

b. With the exception of the 200-meter event, the average speed decreases as distance increases.

c. It takes some time for a runner to accelerate (increase speed) from a speed of zero to his or her running speed. This time, which takes about three seconds, constitutes nearly one-third of the time of a 100-meter race but only about one-sixth of the time of a 200-meter event. Once a runner reaches maximum running speed, he or she can maintain that speed almost as well for 200 meters as for 100 meters.

d. See Figure T3.1a and T3.1b on page 45.

e. Answers will vary, but should be reasonably close to the actual values which are:

1000 m/132.18 s = 7.57 m/s
25000 m/4435.8 s = 5.64 m/s

4. a. (1) The runner's time is a bit less than one-fourth that of the swimmer. Consequently, the runner's speed is a bit more than four times that of the swimmer.

(2) The skater's time is a bit more than one-half that of the runner. Consequently, the skater's speed is a bit less than twice that of the runner.

(3) The skater's time is about one-eighth that of the swimmer. Consequently, the skater's speed is about eight times that of the swimmer.

b. swimmer: 1500 m/883.48 s = 1.70 m/s

runner: 1500 m/207.37 s = 7.23 m/s

skater: 1500 m/111.29 s = 13.48 m/s

c. Answers will vary, but calculations show:

runner: swimmer = 7.23/1.70 = 4.25 ≈ 4+

skater: runner = 13.48/7.23 = 1.86 ≈ 2–

skater: swimmer = 13.48/1.70 = 7.93 ≈ 8

5. a. 8.5 m̶ × 3.28 ft/m̶ = 27.88 ft or 27 ft 10.6 inches.

b. 8.96 – 8.50 = 0.46 m (1.5 feet)

c. 8.50/8.96 × 100 = 94.9%

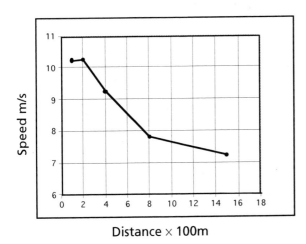

Figure T3.1a

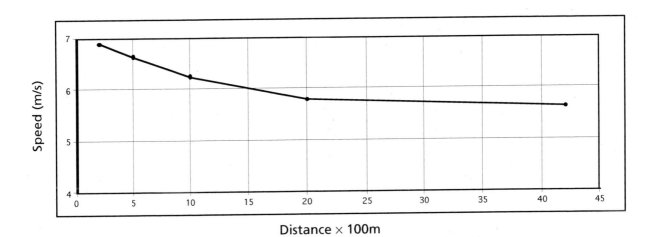

Figure T3.1b

16. What's My Fielding Percentage?

Baseball and softball players are usually interested in measuring how they are performing. For professionals, performance may be the deciding factor in salary negotiations. Many different statistics are kept by baseball fans and players. Some are cumulative—they just add up—like how many Runs Batted In (RBIs) they have or how many errors. Other statistics are the result of division. Examples of these statistics include Batting Averages, Earned Run Averages (ERAs) and Fielding Percentages.

Look at some statistics for former major league shortstop Rabbit Maranville. In his 23-year career, he managed 5139 assists (throws resulting in an out) and 7354 putouts (catches resulting in an out). In all, he made 631 errors. You can determine his "fielding percentage" by using your calculator and the formula:

(Assists + Putouts) ÷ (Errors + Assists + Putouts) = Fielding Percentage

In Rabbit Maranville's case, the formula above would give us:

(5139 + 7354) ÷ (631 + 5139 + 7354) = 12493 ÷ 13124 = .9519201463.

Like batting averages, fielding percentages are usually rounded off to three figures. Maranville's career fielding percentage then, is given as .952 in most baseball statistic books. Baseball players and fans understand that all fielding percentages are less than 1.000, so they often don't mention the decimal point, saying "his fielding percentage was 952."

With a phrase like "fielding percentage," you might expect this number to be shown as a percent, maybe 95%. But fielding percentages are actually expressed as decimals to three places.

Another way to express a fielding percentage is errorless chances per total chances. Whenever you see the word "per" in a problem requiring math for its solution, it means you are going to have to divide one number by another. If someone tells you that gasoline is selling for $1.50 per gallon, or $1.50 ÷ 1 gallon, each gallon costs $1.50. If a baseball player has 495 successful fielding chances per 500 total chances, his or her errorless chances per total chances is 495 ÷ 500 = .990, or a fielding percentage of 990. Another way of saying this is that the player can be expected to make an error about once in every 100 chances, because 99 ÷ 100 = .990.

(continued)

16. What's My Fielding Percentage? *(continued)*

▼ ▼ ▼ ▼ ▼ ▼ ▼ ▼ ▼ ▼ ▼ ▼ ▼ ▼ ▼ ▼ ▼ ▼

If you are working in groups, divide into pairs. Each individual can then determine his or her fielding percentage. After your partner checks your calculation, do questions 2, 3, and 4. Then gather in groups of four to compare your answers and work out any differences you may have.

Once you reach agreement on the answers to questions 1–4, again break up into pairs to work on questions 5–10. Then meet once more in groups of four to compare answers and work out any differences.

▼ ▼ ▼ ▼ ▼ ▼ ▼ ▼ ▼ ▼ ▼ ▼ ▼ ▼ ▼ ▼ ▼ ▼

1. If you are a softball or baseball player, calculate your current fielding percentage or your fielding percentage from last season. Remember that simply catching the ball does not count, only plays that result in outs or errors. If you are not a player yourself, consider the career statistics of Willie Mays as a center fielder (below), and calculate his fielding percentage:

Putouts	Assists	Errors
3328	117	82

   Fielding percentage: _____

2. In 1971, right fielder Roberto Clemente played his next-to-last season for the Pittsburgh Pirates before his death in an airplane accident. That year he managed 267 putouts, 11 assists, and made only 4 errors. What was his fielding percentage that year? _____

3. Also in 1971, Brooks Robinson of the Baltimore Orioles, often considered the best fielding third basemen of all time, had 131 putouts, 354 assists, and 16 errors. What was his fielding percentage in 1971? _____

4. Compare the fielding records of Clemente and Robinson for 1971. Explain why you think that fielding percentages are not *all* that is involved in determining the finest fielders in the game. _____

   _____

   _____

(continued)

16. **What's My Fielding Percentage?** *(continued)*

5. Compare the career fielding percentages of two famous catchers:

   Roy Campanella of the Brooklyn Dodgers (1948–1957) –
   6520 putouts, 550 assists, and 85 errors.
   Fielding percentage: _____

   Johnny Bench of the Cincinnati Reds (1967–1983) –
   9260 putouts, 850 assists, and 97 errors.
   Fielding percentage: _____

6. Kiki Cuyler, a center fielder for several clubs in the 1920's and 1930's had 4034 putouts, 191 assists, and 121 errors in his career. What was his fielding percentage?

7. In 1996, Alex Rodriguez of the Seattle Mariners won the American League batting championship with a .358 average. During the season he also had 239 putouts, 403 assists, and 15 errors. What was his fielding percentage?

8. In the same year, Rodriguez's teammate, Ken Griffey, Jr., had 374 putouts, 10 assists, and 4 errors. What was his fielding percentage? _____

9. In 1996, Chicago Cubs led the National League in fielding. During the season they had 4369 putouts, 1797 assists, and 104 errors. What was the Cubs' team fielding percentage? _____

10. Hall of Famer Ty Cobb, who played major league baseball for 24 years in the early part of the 20th Century, holds the best career batting average in history at .366. His defense was not as good. He garnered 6362 putouts, 392 assists, and 271 errors in all. What was his career fielding percentage?

17. What's My Earned Run Average?

Pitchers are statistics followers too. One of the most commonly reported pitching statistics is Earned Run Average or ERA. This number is the average number of earned runs—runs scored without the aid of an error—the pitcher has given up per nine-inning game.

For instance, Eppa Rixey, a pitcher from 1912 to 1933, pitched 4494 innings in his major league career. In those innings he surrendered 1572 earned runs. To calculate Rixey's ERA, we must take his number of innings and divide by 9 to determine how many full "games" he pitched. Then take the number of runs he gave up and divide it by the number of full games he pitched.

In Rixey's case we get $4494 \div 9 = 499.33333$, and $1572 \div 499.3333 = 3.15$. An earned run average is usually listed with two digits after the decimal point.

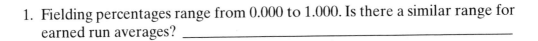

If you are working in groups, divide into pairs. Each individual should then do the following six problems. When you have finished, compare answers with your partner. Then gather again in groups of four to compare your answers and work out any differences you may have.

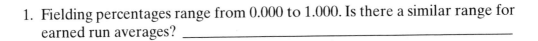

1. Fielding percentages range from 0.000 to 1.000. Is there a similar range for earned run averages? _____

2. After the 1919 season the American League champions, the Chicago White Sox, were heavily favored to win the World Series. They lost the Series. It was later learned that some of the players had conspired to lose on purpose. They were thrown out of baseball for life. One of these infamous "Chicago Black Sox" was pitcher Eddie Cicotte. In his career, he pitched 3224 innings and gave up 848 earned runs. What was his career ERA?

(continued)

17. What's My Earned Run Average? *(continued)*

3. Firpo Marberry was a pitcher for the Washington Senators, Detroit Tigers, and New York Giants in the 1920's and 1930's. He pitched 2066 innings and gave up 834 earned runs. What was his career ERA?

_____

4. Hal Newhouser of the Detroit Tigers was the only pitcher to win the Most Valuable Player Award in back-to-back seasons, in 1944 and 1945. During those two seasons he pitched 625 innings and gave up 140 earned runs. What was his MVP ERA?

_____

5. Sandy Koufax and Bob Gibson were two of the best National League pitchers of the 1960's. In Koufax's 12-year career, before succumbing to arthritis, he pitched 2325 innings and gave up 713 earned runs. Gibson pitched for 17 years, racking up 3885 innings and yielding 1258 earned runs. Compare the ERA's of these two great hurlers.

Koufax: _____

Gibson: _____

6. Louis Walter "Kid" Bauer pitched in one game for the Philadelphia Athletics in 1918. In his one appearance in a major league game, he gave up 2 runs without getting any outs. He was therefore credited with an unusual ERA. What was it?

_____

18. In the Sports Pages

There's a lot of math in the sports pages of your newspaper. Below is one example. You can find many more by reading about your favorite sports in newspapers, magazines, and books.

The table below shows the standings at one point in time for the Eastern Division of the Canadian Football League (CFL). The column headings W, L, T, F, A, and Pts stand for games Won, games Lost, games Tied, points scored For (by) the team, points scored Against the team, and Points acquired by the team thus far in the season.

CFL Eastern Division						
Team	**W**	**L**	**T**	**F**	**A**	**Pts**
Hamilton	3	0	0	96	60	6
Toronto	2	1	0	76	74	4
Montreal	1	1	1	42	50	3
Ottawa	0	2	1	42	72	1

▼ ▼ ▼ ▼ ▼ ▼ ▼ ▼ ▼ ▼ ▼ ▼ ▼ ▼ ▼ ▼ ▼

If you are working in groups, divide into pairs. Each individual should then do all the problems. When you have finished, compare answers with your partner. Then gather again in the larger group to compare answers and work out any differences you may have.

▼ ▼ ▼ ▼ ▼ ▼ ▼ ▼ ▼ ▼ ▼ ▼ ▼ ▼ ▼ ▼ ▼

1. At the time of the standings shown in the table, what percentage of the games it had played had each of the following teams won?

    a. Hamilton: _____

    b. Toronto: _____

    c. Montreal: _____

    d. Ottawa: _____

(continued)

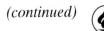

18. In the Sports Pages *(continued)*

2. At the time of the standings shown, which team would you think had:

   a. the best offense: _____

   b. the best defense: _____

   c. Explain your answers to a. and b. above.

   _____

   _____

   _____

3. Using the standings, how many points does a team receive for each:

   a. win: _____

   b. tie: _____

   c. loss: _____

4. What was the average number of points scored per game by Hamilton after playing three games? _____

5. What was the average number of points per game allowed by Montreal's defense after playing 3 games? _____

6. Should the total for column F (points scored by all teams) equal the total for column A (points scored against all teams)? _____

   Add the two columns. Are they equal? _____

19. More in the Sports Pages

This table gives the standings for American League Teams at the all-star break in July 1996. In the table, the W column gives the games won by each team listed; the L column gives the games lost by each team; the Pct. column gives the decimal fraction of games won for all games played; the GB (games behind) column indicates the number of games that each team trails the team in first place. The American League has three divisions—East, Central, and West. On July 10, 1996, New York led the East, Cleveland was in first place in the Central division, and the Texas Rangers led the West.

American League Teams: July 10, 1996				
East	**W**	**L**	**Pct**	**GB**
New York	52	33	.612	___
Baltimore	46	39	___	6
Toronto	38	49	___	15
Boston	36	49	___	___
Detroit	27	61	___	___
Central	**W**	**L**	**Pct**	**GB**
Cleveland	52	35	___	___
Chicago	50	37	___	___
Milwaukee	43	43	___	$8\frac{1}{2}$
Minnesota	41	45	___	___
West	**W**	**L**	**Pct**	**GB**
Texas	51	36	___	___
Seattle	46	39	___	___
California	43	45	___	___
Oakland	43	45	___	$8\frac{1}{2}$

(continued)

Middle School Math You Really Need

19. More in the Sports Pages *(continued)*

If you are working in groups, divide into pairs. You should work out the Pct. for each team in one or more of the three divisions (East, Central, or West). Your partner should do the same. Then compare answers with your partner before the entire group meets to compare results for the entire league. Work out any differences you may have. Repeat the procedure for question 2.

1. Fill in the blanks in the Pct. column.

2. The GB (games behind) column indicates the combined number of games that the trailing team must win and the first-place team must lose in order for the trailing team to catch up to the leading team. It can be calculated as follows:

$$\frac{(\text{lead team's wins} - \text{trailing team's wins}) + (\text{trailing team's losses} - \text{lead team's losses})}{2}$$

For example, Seattle was 4 games behind Texas:

$$\frac{(51-46) + (39-36)}{2} = \frac{(5+3)}{2} = 4$$

If Texas were to lose 4 games and Seattle win 4, the standings would be even.

	W	**L**	**GB**
Texas	51	40	—
Seattle	50	39	—

$$\frac{(51-50) + (39-40)}{2} = \frac{[1 + (-1)]}{2} = 0$$

Of course, Texas has played two more games than Seattle (91 vs. 89). If this were the end of the season, the outcome would depend on what Seattle did in its last two games. It could win one and lose one and tie Texas, lose both and lose the division title, or win 2 and win the title.

3. Return to the table of league standings and determine the GB (games behind the first-place team) for each team where that calculation has not been done.

20. Still More from the Sports Pages

This table gives attendance figures for American League Baseball teams from opening day to the all-star break in July, 1996. This is about half the baseball season. The table gives the total number of games (dates) played at home, the total number of fans who attended these games, and the average number of people attending each game (number per game) for Baltimore and Boston.

Attendance Figures for the first half of the 1996 American League Baseball season.			
Team	**Dates**	**Total attendance**	**Average attendance**
Baltimore	46	2,038,534	44,316
Boston	41	1,133,451	27,645
California	44	1,054,715	_____
Chicago	40	843,836	_____
Cleveland	44	1,839,190	_____
Detroit	43	638,789	_____
Kansas City	43	781,556	_____
Milwaukee	40	585,510	_____
Minnesota	44	766,877	_____
New York	45	1,119,291	_____
Oakland	41	516,942	_____
Seattle	44	1,455,177	_____
Texas	46	1,610,768	_____
Toronto	41	1,289,964	_____
A.L. Totals	___	_____	_____
N.L. Totals	601	16,009,881	26,639

(continued)

20. Still More from the Sports Pages (continued)

▼ ▼ ▼ ▼ ▼ ▼ ▼ ▼ ▼ ▼ ▼ ▼ ▼ ▼ ▼ ▼ ▼ ▼ ▼

If you are working in groups, check your individual answers to question 1. Then divide up the calculations for question 2 so that each individual has to do no more than six. Be sure that at least two people do each team so they can check each other's answers.

Once there is agreement about question 2, divide into pairs to answer question 3. One member of the pair can read the numbers while the second uses a calculator to add the figures. Compare results in your larger groups and work out any differences before discussing the answers to question 4 as a large group.

▼ ▼ ▼ ▼ ▼ ▼ ▼ ▼ ▼ ▼ ▼ ▼ ▼ ▼ ▼ ▼ ▼ ▼ ▼

1. Check the average attendance figures for Baltimore and Boston. Do the figures in the tables agree with your calculations? _____

2. Fill in the average attendance column by calculating the average attendance figures for the other American League teams (California to Toronto).

3. Find the total games (dates) played by all American League teams for the first half of the season. Then fill in the blank beside A. L. (American League) Totals. Do the same for total attendance. Then calculate the league's average attendance figure and fill in that blank.

4. How do the totals for dates and attendance for the American League compare with those given for the National League?

_____

_____

_____

_____

_____

21. Math at the Olympics

Every four years some of the world's greatest athletes compete at the Olympic Games. At these games, world records are often broken. In 1996, the Summer Olympic Games were held in Atlanta, Georgia. Records were broken in a number of sports.

▼ ▼ ▼ ▼ ▼ ▼ ▼ ▼ ▼ ▼ ▼ ▼ ▼ ▼ ▼ ▼ ▼ ▼ ▼ ▼

If you are working in groups, work individually on questions 1 and 2. Then compare your results with your partner's and with the entire group's before moving on to question 3.

In part 3a, the calculations of speed can be shared by members of the entire group. But be sure each calculation is done by more than one person so that answers can be checked. Once there is agreement about the speeds in question 3a, the rest of the question can be answered individually and checked by a partner.

Questions 4 and 5 can be answered individually and then checked with a partner before the entire group meets to compare results and discuss any differences.

▼ ▼ ▼ ▼ ▼ ▼ ▼ ▼ ▼ ▼ ▼ ▼ ▼ ▼ ▼ ▼ ▼ ▼ ▼

1. At the 1996 Olympics in Atlanta, Donovan Bailey of Canada set a world record for the 100-meter dash with a time of 9.84 seconds.

   a. What was Bailey's average speed, in meters per second, during the race?

   b. There are 3.28 feet in a meter. What was Bailey's average speed in feet per second? _____

   c. There are 5,280 feet in a mile. What was Bailey's speed in miles per hour?

   d. A century earlier, at the 1896 Olympic Games, Thomas Burke of the United States won the 100-meter dash with a time of 12.0 seconds. What was Burke's speed in meters per second? _____

   e. Compare Bailey's speed to Burke's, that is, divide Bailey's speed by Burke's speed. How many times faster was Bailey? _____

   f. What was Burke's speed in miles per hour? _____

(continued)

21. Math at the Olympics *(continued)*

2. At the 1996 Olympic Games, Michael Johnson of the United States set a world record for the 200-meter event. His time was 19.32 seconds.

   a. What was Johnson's average speed in meters per second? _____

   b. What was Johnson's speed in miles per hour? _____

   c. In 1900, Walter Tewksbury of the United States won the 200-meter event with a time of 22.2 seconds. What was Tewksbury's average speed, in meters per second, during his race? _____

   d. Compare Tewksbury's speed to Johnson's; that is, divide Tewksbury's speed by Johnson's speed. How many times faster was Johnson?

   _____

   e. Divide Tewksbury's time by Johnson's time. How does your result compare with your answer to part d? _____

3. The table below shows the record times for races of distances ranging from 100 meters to the marathon (42.2 kilometers or 26.2 miles).

Distance (in meters)	Record time (in seconds)	Speed (m/s)	Distance (in meters)	Record time (in seconds)	Speed (m/s)
100	9.84	_____	2000	287.88	_____
200	19.32	_____	5000	764.39	_____
400	43.29	_____	10000	1603.63	_____
800	101.73	_____	20000	3415.6	_____
1000	132.18	_____	25000	4435.8	_____
1500	207.37	_____	marathon	7610	_____

   a. Calculate the record average speed for each race in meters per second.

   _____

   b. What happens to a runner's average speed as the distance of the race increases?

   c. How can you explain the fact that the speed for the 200-meter event is greater than the speed for the 100-meter event? _____

   _____

   _____

   _____

(continued)

21. Math at the Olympics *(continued)*

d. To see in graphical form how the distance of an event and a runner's speed are related, you can plot two graphs of speed vs. time. The axes for the first graph, for distances from 100 to 1500 m, are given in Figure 3.1. The axes for the second graph, for distances from 2000 m to the marathon, are given in Figure 3.2. You can plot the points for each graph using the speeds you calculated from the times and distances in the table.

Draw the best curved line you can through the points you have plotted for each graph.

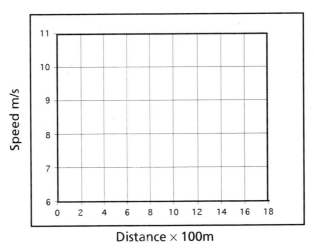

Figure 3.1

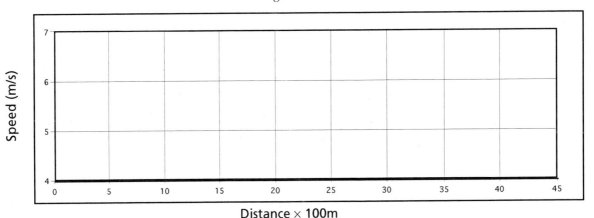

Figure 3.2

e. Use the graphs you have made to predict the approximate average record speeds for the 1000 m and 25000 m events.

1000 m: _____

2500 m: _____

(continued)

         Middle School Math You Really Need

21. Math at the Olympics *(continued)*

4. This table gives some winning times for the 1500-meter event in swimming, running, and skating.

Mode of motion	Time to move 1500 m (s)
swimming (freestyle)	883.48
running (dash)	207.37
skating (speed)	111.29

a. Based on the times alone, estimate (don't calculate):

(1) a good runner's speed compared to that of a good swimmer

_____

(2) a good skater's speed compared to that of a good runner

_____

(3) a good skater's speed compared to that of a good swimmer

_____

b. Calculate the actual speeds of swimmer, runner, and skater in meters per second (m/s) from the information in the table.

swimmer _____

runner _____

skater _____

c. Based on your calculations of speed in part b, how good were your estimates in part a?_____

5. At the 1996 Olympic Games, Carl Lewis of the United States won his fourth consecutive gold medal for the long jump with a leap of 8.50 meters. The world's record for the long jump was set by Mike Powell of the United States in 1991. Powell jumped 8.96 meters.

a. What was Lewis's leap in feet and inches? _____

b. By how much did Lewis miss equaling the world record with his 1996 jump?

c. What percentage of the world's record was Lewis's jump? _____

CHAPTER 4   Math with Big and Significant Numbers

To the Teacher

Not all numbers are significant. If someone tells you the distance from your home to your school is 16.01456 miles, you will be satisfied to know that it's 16 miles. The decimal fraction following the 16 has little meaning to you. However, those numbers may or may not have mathematical significance. If the measurement of the distance was made to ± 0.00001 mile, then the numbers in the decimal fraction are significant. If the measurement was made by pacing off the distance by foot, even the second digit (the 6) may be questionable.

Students generally are fascinated by big numbers, which is one reason for introducing them here. But big numbers are also used in astronomy—another subject that many students find interesting—and in estimating the age of the universe, the age of the earth, and the time when dinosaurs roamed the earth. Dinosaurs seem to capture the attention of most students.

22. Numbers That Mean Something: Significant Figures

(page 67)

Handheld calculators do not help students understand significant figures. They do just the opposite. When adding numbers, the calculator does not hesitate to add 23.7654 cm. to 12.7 cm. and read out 36.4654 cm, even though a measurement of 12.7 cm. is only reli-

able to ± 0.1 cm, certainly not to ± 0.0001 cm. Likewise, division and multiplication are only as good as the least accurate measurement, which is seldom the same as all the numbers shown on the calculator's display when multiplication or division are performed.

Answers

1. a. 2
   b. 3
   c. 3
   d. 3. The first two zeros are used to place the decimal; they are not significant figures. We could just as well have written 468 ten-thousandths of a millimeter.
   e. 7

2. a. $1.15 \text{ m} \times 0.32 \text{ m} \times 0.825 \text{ m} = 0.30 \text{ m}^3$
   b. $0.30 \text{ m}^3 \times 2412 \text{ kg/m}^3 = 720 \text{ kg}$

3. $31 \text{ cm} \times 30.2 \text{ cm} \times 60.67 \text{ cm} = 56799.254 \text{ cm}^3$, which to two significant figures equals 57,000 cm^3

4. $13.6 + 12.665 + 2.75 = 29.015 = 29.0$ (rounded to tenths, as in the least accurate number—13.6)

5. $65.9876 \text{ m} + 1246.765 \text{ m} + 44.9 \text{ m} = 1357.7 \text{ m}$

6. $45.149 \text{ cm}/4 = 11.28725 \text{ cm} = 11.287 \text{ cm}$ to 5 significant figures

7. 42765.654 m/3.8745 m = 11037.722 = 11,038 to 5 significant figures

8. 16.9172 g ÷ 3.68 mL = 4.5970652 = 4.60 g/mL to three significant figures

9. a. 9.6 cm × 8.6 cm = 82.56 cm^2 = 83 cm^2 to 2 significant figures

    b. 9.4 cm × 8.4 cm = 78.96 cm^2 = 79 cm^2 to 2 significant figures

    c. 9.5 cm × 8.5 cm = 80.75 cm^2 = 81 cm^2 to 2 significant figures

23. Numbers for Astronomers
(page 70)

In addition to helping students learn about how big numbers can be expressed as powers of ten and coefficients times a power of ten, this section will reinforce what they learned earlier about significant figures, and it will prepare them for the vast distances and time found in the sections that follow.

Students may enjoy writing their own drill problems with regard to powers of ten and scientific notation.

You might like to point out to students that scientific notation can fool us. We may think we understand a number because we can easily write it in scientific notation. But do we always understand it?

The present size of the universe is estimated to be 10^{23} kilometers. But just what does that mean? We can write the value in various ways:

1.0×10^{23} km;
100,000,000,000,000,000,000,000 km; or as
1,000,000,000,000,000,000,000 × 10 km.

We know that it's five times larger than 2×10^{22}, three times larger than 3.3×10^{22}, and twice as large as 5×10^{22}, etc.

We know that every time we add a 0 to a number we are multiplying it by 10. And we can probably comprehend

$10^2 \times 10 = 10^3$, (1,000), but a number like 1,000,000,000,000,000,000,000,000 is beyond our understanding. It's easy to write 10×10^{22} or 1.0×10^{23}, but not so simple when we write 10,000,000,000,000,000,000,000 × 10 = 100,000,000,000,000,000,000,000.

To reinforce what you have said, ask them, "What is the size of the universe in light years (ly)?"

A light year is the distance light travels in one year. Since light travels at 3.0×10^5 km/s, we can find the distance light travels in a year by multiplying its speed by the number of seconds in one year. The number of seconds in one year is: 3600 s/h × 24 h/d × 365 d/y = 3.15×10^7 s/y. Therefore, a light year is: 3.15×10^7 s × 3.0×10^5 km/s = 9.5×10^{12} km or approximately 10^{13} km.

The size of the universe in light years then is approximately 10^{23} km ÷ 10^{13} km/ly = 10^{10} ly or

TEN BILLION LIGHT YEARS!

We cannot really relate to such a distance whether expressed in kilometers or in light years. Even the speed of light exceeds our imagination. We can't comprehend such a speed because nothing in our experience even approaches such a speed. Jet planes only travel at about 800 km/h or 800 km/hr × 1 h/3600 s = 0.22 km/s, just a bit more than two tenths of a kilometer per second (0.14 mi/s). This is negligible when compared to 300,000 kilometers per second!

Answers

1. a. 100,000 = 10^5

    b. 1,000,000 = 10^6

    c. 100,000,000 = 10^8

    d. 1,000,000,000,000,000 = 10^{15}

2. a. 5×10^3 = 5,000

    b. 4.7×10^5 = 470,000

c. $7.9 \times 10^6 = 7,900,000$

d. $6.8 \times 10^9 = 6,800,000,000$

e. $3.1 \times 10^2 = 310$

f. $6.5432 \times 10^4 = 65,432$

3. a. $10^2 \times 10^7 = 10^9$

   b. $10^{12} \times 10^{23} = 10^{35}$

   c. $(2 \times 10^5) \times (3 \times 10^9) = 6 \times 10^{14}$

   d. $(2.3 \times 10^3) \times (3.5 \times 10^8) = 8.1 \times 10^{11}$

   e. $(4.12 \times 10^3 \times (3.4 \times 10^{24}) = 14 \times 10^{27}$
      or 1.4×10^{28}

   f. $(3.45 \times 10^6) \times (8.54 \times 10^5) = 29.5 \times 10^{11}$ or 2.95×10^{12}

4. a. $10^7 \div 10^2 = 10^5$

   b. $10^{24} \div 10^{21} = 10^3$

   c. $(4 \times 10^9) \div (2 \times 10^5) = 2 \times 10^4$

   d. $(3.5 \times 10^8) \div (2.3 \times 10^3) = 1.5 \times 10^5$

   e. $(4.12 \times 10^{24} \div (3.4 \times 10^3) = 1.2 \times 10^{21}$

   f. $(3.45 \times 10^6) \div (8.54 \times 10^5) = 0.404 \times 10^1$ or $4.04 \times 10^0 = 4.04$

5. 60 s/min × 60 min/hr × 24 hr/da × 365.25 da/yr = 31,557,600 s/yr or 3.1558×10^7 s/yr

6. 2.9979×10^5 km/s × 3.1558×10^7 s/yr = 9.4608×10^{12} km/yr

7. $\$5.0 \times 10^{12}/2.5 \times 10^8$ people = $\$2.0 \times 10^4$/person

8. a. 6.0×10^{23} molecules ÷ 2.4×10^1 L = 2.5×10^{22} molecules/L

   b. 6.0×10^{23} molecules ÷ $(2.4 \times 10^1$ L × 1.0×10^3 mL/L) = 2.5×10^{19} molecules/mL

9. a. 4.0130×10^4 km

   b. 3.84403×10^5 km

   c. $1.49597870 \times 10^{11}$ m

24. *Models of the Solar System and the Universe* (page 74)

For astronomers, as well as others such as economists and citizens who must confront the national debt, using large numbers is part of everyday work. A model of the universe is not *Math You Really Need* for most people, but it is included here because it is so essential to understanding basic astronomy and the universe we all live in and because it is a way of providing insight into the use of exponents. We think your students will enjoy it, for it will certainly increase their awareness of the vast nature of the universe and the tiny size of the planets relative to the sun.

The model of the universe that can be constructed from the data cannot be made or shown to scale. To see why, consider our sun's diameter, which is about 1.39×10^6 kilometers (864,000 miles). The diameter of an average galaxy is 10^{18} km—about 10^{12} times as great—impossible to show on a scaled model.

Answers

1. By dividing known numbers in one column that correspond to those in another, students can calculate the numbers that belong in the blanks. Their results should be similar to, but not necessarily identical to those shown in the completed table on page 64.

Object	Diameter (in km)	Relative diameter (Earth = 1.0)	Diameter of object in model	Radius of orbit (km)	Radius of orbit (A.U.)	Radius of orbit in model
Sun	1.4×10^6	108	24 cm	NA	NA	NA
Mercury	5.2×10^3	0.38	0.8 mm	5.8×10^7	0.39	9.9 m
Venus	1.3×10^4	0.95	2.1 mm	1.1×10^8	0.72	18 m
Earth	1.3×10^4	1.0	2.2 mm	1.5×10^8	1.0	25 m
Mars	6.8×10^3	0.52	1.2 mm	2.3×10^8	1.52	38 m
Jupiter	1.4×10^5	10.8	24 mm	7.8×10^8	5.2	130 m
Saturn	1.2×10^5	9.2	20 mm	1.4×10^9	9.5	238 m
Uranus	5.4×10^4	4.1	9 mm	2.9×10^9	19.3	483 m
Neptune	5.0×10^4	3.8	8.4 mm	4.5×10^9	30.0	750 m
Pluto	2.6×10^3	0.2	0.4 mm	5.9×10^9	39.3	983 m

2. One big glob or circle can represent the universe. Smaller globs or circles (not drawn to any scale) within the universe can represent galaxies. Inside the galactal globs or circles are the stars represented by dots or small circles. The galactal systems should be labeled as about 100 galactal diameters apart. This is 10^{18} km $\times 10^2 = 10^{20}$ km. Stars are about 10^6 km in diameter, which when multiplied by their separation (10^8 star diameters) makes them about 10^{14} km apart, on the average.

3. The average spacing of galaxies is 10^2 galactal diameters, whereas the average star spacing is about 10^8 star diameters. Galaxies are much closer together than stars, when considered on their own scales and are, therefore, much more likely to collide than stars.

25. Big Bang, Life, Dinosaurs, Humans, and a Time Line
(page 76)

Student groups will need a sheet of paper large enough for a one meter time line.

A period covering over 230 million years can be drawn on a 12-inch line if 20 million years is represented by an inch. The information needed for the time line is all in the text—the students do not have to go to other sources.

Answers

1. See Figure T4.1.

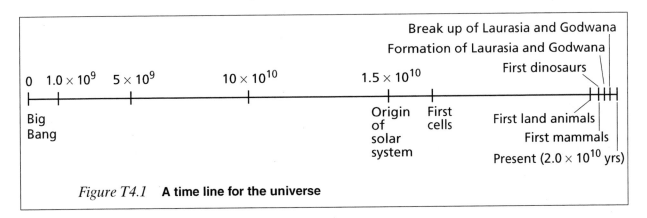

Figure T4.1 **A time line for the universe**

2. a. 2.0×10^6 yr$/1.0 \times 10^2$ cm$= 2.0 \times 10^4$ yr/cm.

   b. See Figure T4.2.

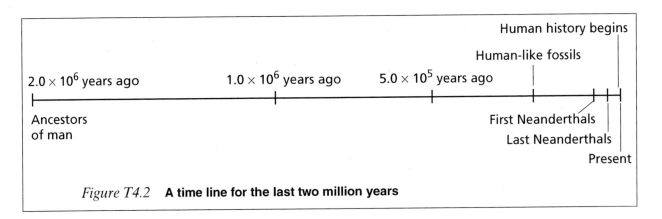

Figure T4.2 **A time line for the last two million years**

c. There are 3.16×10^7 seconds in one year and 2.0×10^{10} yr $\div 3.16 \times 10^7$ s $= 6.3 \times 10^2$ yr/s. So each second represents about 630 years. On this scale humans have been around for 6.0×10^4 yr $\div 6.3 \times 10^2$ yr/s = 95 seconds. They have recorded history for 6.0×10^3 yr $\div 6.3 \times 10^2$ yr/s = 9.5 seconds. Assuming a student's age to be about 12 years, he or she has been around 12 yr $\div$ 6.3×10^2 yr/s = 0.019 seconds.

d. There are 86,400 seconds in a day $(60 \times 60 \times 24)$. 2.0×10^{10} yr$/8.64 \times 10^4$ s $= 2.3 \times 10^5$ yr/s, so each second represents 2.3×10^5 years. On this scale humans have been around for 6.0×10^4 yr $\div 2.3 \times 10^5$ yr/s = 0.26 second and have recorded history for only 0.026 second. Assuming a student's age to be about 12 years, he or she has been around 12 yr $\div$ 2.3×10^5 yr/s = 0.00005 s.

26. *Kuiper Belt* (page 78)

You might like to read the *Scientific American* reference on the Kuiper belt, a very new concept: *Sci. Am. May, 1996, 46–52.*

Answers

1. The Oort belt lies between 3000 AU and 100,000 AU from the sun, or between 3000 and 100,000 cm on this scale. This works out to be a sphere of average radius 0.5 km (0.8 mi). The Kuiper belt will begin at only 40 cm from the sun, and forms a plane tilted to the plane of the ecliptic. Pluto lies in the Kuiper belt.

2. The inner solar system of planets lies between 0.4 cm (Mercury) and 1.6 cm (Mars), forming a plane with all rotating in the same direction. The outer solar system of planets stretches from about 5 to 40 AU, (5–40 cm), also lying in the plane of the ecliptic and rotating in the same direction as the inner planets.

3. All of the bodies of the solar system would be smaller than the tiniest flick of dust when 1 cm is allowed to represent 1 AU (150,000,000 km or 93,000,000 mi). Even the sun would be only 0.01 cm in diameter.

22. Numbers That Mean Something: Significant Figures

Addition and Subtraction:

Suppose we measure a metal bar with a ruler and find it to be 12.5 cm long. Then we use a very accurate micrometer to measure another bar and find 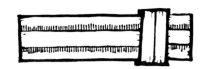 it to be 4.8337 cm long. The 12.5 cm bar is only known to the nearest tenth of a centimeter: ± (+ or −) 0.1 cm. This is true because the measuring device is divided into lines that are 1 centimeter apart. We estimate the bar's length to lie halfway between 12 and 13 cm. The 4.8337 cm measurement was made with a fine caliper that can read to ± 0.0001 cm. The "weakest" (least accurate) measurement is the tenths of a centimeter in the 12.5 cm measurement. If we want to add the two lengths, the fine caliper measurement need only be used to the same fractional part of a centimeter, tenths. We do not know the hundredths, thousandths, and ten-thousandths for the 12.5 cm bar. Since we estimated the tenths (0.5) in the 12.5 cm measurement, we have no way of knowing what the hundredths figure is unless we use a more accurate measuring instrument. Thus, to add the two measurements, we include only the first figure to the right of the decimal point in the more accurate measurement:

12.5???

+ 4.8~~337~~

17.3 cm

We say the measurement is good to 17.3 cm, which contains three significant figures. The more accurate measurement (4.8337) contained five significant figures.

The same sort of reasoning determines the use of significant figures in subtraction.

Multiplication and Division:

Suppose you find that the area of a certain town is 50.4 square miles. According to a recent census, the population of the town is 5021. To find the population density (the number of people per square mile), you divide 5021 people by 50.4 square miles. Your calculator gives you an answer of 99.623016. Can you say that the population density is 99.623016 people per square mile?

In measuring anything, you finally come to a point where you have to estimate the number in the measurement. The last number in any recorded measurement is an estimate. It is determined by estimating a point between two lines on a ruler, a telescope, a microscope, transit, or whatever measuring instrument is being used. Any digit that represents an actual measurement is a significant figure.

(continued)

22. Numbers That Mean Something: Significant Figures

(continued)

Dividing or multiplying two measurements does not make them more accurate. As a general rule, the number of significant figures in the quotient or product of two or more numbers cannot be greater than the number of significant figures in the least accurate of the measurements. If you wanted to multiply a number with 5 significant figures and one with 2 significant figures, the product would have 2 significant figures.

$$2.3456 \text{ cm} \times 4.1 \text{ cm} = 9.6 \text{ cm}^2 \quad \textbf{not} \quad 9.61696 \text{ cm}^2$$

To see why, remember that the one-tenth in 4.1 was an estimate; the measurement could be closer to 4.0 cm or to 4.2 cm. If you multiply 2.3456 by 4.0 and then by 4.2, you find:

$$2.3456 \times 4.\underline{\textbf{0}} = 9.\underline{\textbf{3}}824$$

$$2.3456 \times 4.\underline{\textbf{2}} = 9.\underline{\textbf{8}}5152$$

The underlined numbers in bold print on 4.0 and 4.2 show the first estimated figure in the measurements. The underlined numbers in bold print for 9.3824 and 9.85152 show the first numbers that differ in the two products. A product cannot be more accurate than the least accurate number used to obtain it. Only the 9 is common to both products for the two multiplications shown. It is in the second digit that the answers differ. This is reasonable because it was the second figure that was estimated in the original measurement of the less accurate value. So we can say that the product has the same number of significant figures (2) as the least accurate measurement.

Now, let's go back to the question about population density. The area of the town was only measured to three significant figures. Therefore, the population density should be expressed as 99.6 people per square mile. The figures to the right of the 6 are not significant.

The following questions will help you to understand significant figures.

If you are working in groups, divide into pairs. Do the problems with your partner. Then come back together as a group and compare your answers and solutions. Try to work out any differences you may have. Compare answers with other groups and resolve any differences.

(continued)

22. Numbers That Mean Something: Significant Figures

(continued)

1. How many significant figures are there in the following measurements?

    a. 12 km _____

    b. 127 km _____

    c. 0.468 cm _____

    d. 0.0468 mm _____

    e. 2.503467 km _____

2. A concrete step is 1.15 m long, 0.32 m wide, and 0.825 m thick.

    a. What is the volume of the step? _____

    b. Each cubic meter of concrete weighs 2412 kg. How much does the concrete step weigh? _____

3. A fish tank is 31 cm deep, 30.2 cm wide, and 60.67 cm long. What volume of water will the tank hold? _____

4. 13.6 cm + 12.665 cm + 2.75 cm = _____

5. 65.9876 m + 1246.765 m + 44.9 m = _____

6. Divide a 45.149 cm steel bar into 4 equally long pieces.

7. 42765.654 m ÷ 3.8745 m = _____

8. 16.9172 g ÷ 3.68 mL = _____

9. A ruler is used to mark off a 9.5 cm × 8.5 cm rectangle. Because of errors in drawing and measuring, the area marked off could be as small as 9.4 cm × 8.4 cm or as large as 9.6 cm × 8.6 cm.

    a. What is largest area the rectangle might have? _____

    b. What is the smallest area the rectangle might have? _____

    c. Using the two significant figures 9.5 and 8.5, what is the area of the rectangle?

69 *Middle School Math You Really Need*

23. Numbers for Astronomers

Many scientists, especially astronomers, have to deal with huge numbers. The distances between stars and galaxies are so great that astronomers measure them in light years. A light year is the distance light travels in one year—almost ten trillion kilometers (six trillion miles). A trillion, when written out, is 1,000,000,000,000. Ten trillion is 10,000,000,000,000.

To save time and space, such large numbers may be written using a shorter method. The shorthand method is based on the fact that:

$100 = 10 \times 10$

$1,000 = 10 \times 100 = 10 \times 10 \times 10$

$10,000 = 10 \times 1,000 = 10 \times 10 \times 10 \times 10$

The number 100 (10×10) can also be written 10^2. The little elevated ^{2} to the right of the 10 is called an **exponent** or a **power**. It indicates how many times the 10 is multiplied by itself. Thus, such numbers as 10 (10×1), 100 (10×10), 1,000 ($10 \times 10 \times 10$), 10,000 ($10 \times 10 \times 10 \times 10$), 100,000 ($10 \times 10 \times 10 \times 10 \times 10$), 1,000,000 ($10 \times 10 \times 10 \times 10 \times 10 \times 10$) ... may be written as $10^1, 10^2, 10^3, 10^4, 10^5, 10^6, \ldots$; that is, as powers of ten. The exponent or power indicates the number of zeros that follow one, or the number of times that 10 is multiplied by itself.

If we multiply numbers written as powers of ten, we can simply add the exponents to find the product. For example, $10^2 \times 10^2 = 10^4$ because (10×10) × (10×10) = 10,000 = 10^4. Similarly, $10^3 \times 10^4 = 10^7$ because ($10 \times 10 \times 10$) × ($10 \times 10 \times 10 \times 10$) = 10,000,000 = 10^7.

If we divide numbers written as powers of ten, we can find the dividend by simply subtracting the exponent in the denominator from the exponent in the numerator.

$$\frac{10^5}{10^2} = 10^{5-2} = \frac{10 \times 10 \times 10 \times \cancel{10} \times \cancel{10}}{\cancel{10} \times \cancel{10}} = 10 \times 10 \times 10 = 10^3$$

Two of the tens in the denominator cancel two of the tens in the numerator because $10 \div 10 = 1$. Multiplying or dividing a number by 1 does not change its value.

The number 10 may be written as 10 or as 10^1. Any number raised to the first power is the number itself. For example, $2^1 = 2, 5^1 = 5, 9^1 = 9, 10^1 = 10$.

Any number raised to the zero power is 1. Therefore, $2^0 = 1, 5^0 = 1, 8^0 = 1, 10^0 = 1$. We can show this with an equation:

$$10^4 \div 10^4 = \frac{10 \times 10 \times 10 \times 10}{10 \times 10 \times 10 \times 10} = 10^0 = 1$$

(continued)

Middle School Math You Really Need

23. Numbers for Astronomers *(continued)*

Any number can be written as the product of a number between 1 and 10 (called the **coefficient**) and a power of ten. For example, because 150 is 1.5×100, it can be written as 1.5×10^2. In the same way, 3,200 can be written as 3.2×10^3, 32,000 as 3.2×10^4, and 560,000,000 as 5.6×10^8, and so on. Numbers expressed in this manner are said to be written in **scientific notation**.

The product of two numbers written in scientific notation can be found by multiplying their coefficients and then their powers of ten. For example:

$$3.0 \times 10^6 \times 4.0 \times 10^5 = 12 \times 10^{11} = 1.2 \times 10^{12}$$

To divide numbers written in scientific notation, find the quotient of the coefficients and then the quotient of their powers of ten. For example:

$$2.6 \times 10^4 \text{ m} \div 1.1 \times 10^2 \text{ m} = 2.4 \times 10^2$$

Scientific notation isn't just a shorthand method for writing big numbers. It is also a good way to indicate significant figures. When you see a measurement such as 1200 meters, you cannot be sure how many significant figures it contains. Was the measurement made to ±1 m, ±10 m, or ±100 m? You have no way of knowing. However, if the number is written as 1.200×10^3 m, you know the measurement contains 4 significant figures. The measurement was made to the nearest meter (± 1 m). If written as 1.2×10^3 m, you know there are only 2 significant figures. The measurement is only good to the nearest 100 m (± 100 m). It could be as high as 1.3×10^3 m or as low as 1.1×10^3 m.

▼ ▼ ▼ ▼ ▼ ▼ ▼ ▼ ▼ ▼ ▼ ▼ ▼ ▼ ▼ ▼ ▼ ▼

If you are working in groups, divide into pairs. You can then work on the first four questions and check them with your partner. Then go on and work on the next five questions together. The group can then meet to compare answers, discuss how the questions were solved, and resolve any differences.

▼ ▼ ▼ ▼ ▼ ▼ ▼ ▼ ▼ ▼ ▼ ▼ ▼ ▼ ▼ ▼ ▼ ▼

(continued)

23. Numbers for Astronomers *(continued)*

1. Express the following numbers as powers of ten.
   a. 100,000 _____
   b. 1,000,000 _____
   c. 100,000,000 _____
   d. 1,000,000,000,000,000 _____

2. Write the following numbers using zeros rather than powers of ten.
   a. 5×10^3 _____
   b. 4.7×10^5 _____
   c. 7.9×10^6 _____
   d. 6.8×10^9 _____
   e. 3.1×10^2 _____
   f. 6.5432×10^4 _____

3. Find the following products using powers of ten or scientific notation. Pay attention to significant figures.
   a. $10^2 \times 10^7$ _____
   b. $10^{12} \times 10^{23}$ _____
   c. $(2 \times 10^5) \times (3 \times 10^9)$ _____
   d. $(2.3 \times 10^3) \times (3.5 \times 10^8)$ _____
   e. $(4.12 \times 10^3) \times (3.4 \times 10^{24})$ _____
   f. $(3.45 \times 10^6) \times (8.54 \times 10^5)$ _____

4. Carry out the following divisions using powers of ten or scientific notation. Pay attention to significant figures.
   a. $10^7 \div 10^2$ _____
   b. $10^{24} \div 10^{21}$ _____
   c. $(4 \times 10^9) \div (2 \times 10^5)$ _____
   d. $(3.5 \times 10^8) \div (2.3 \times 10^3)$ _____
   e. $(4.12 \times 10^{24}) \div (3.4 \times 10^3)$ _____
   f. $(3.45 \times 10^6) \div (8.54 \times 10^5)$ _____

(continued)

23. **Numbers for Astronomers** (continued)

5. How many seconds are there in one year (365.25 days)? _____

6. Light travels at a speed of 2.9979×10^5 km/s. How far will light travel in one year?

7. The federal debt is approximately $\$5.0 \times 10^{12}$. The population of the United States is approximately 2.5×10^8 people. What is the national debt in dollars per person? _____

8. At room temperature, 24 liters of a gas is known to contain 6.0×10^{23} molecules of the gas. How many molecules are there in:

   a. 1.0 L of the gas? _____

   b. 1.0 mL of the gas? _____

9. After doing a little research, use scientific notation to write the following numbers:

   a. The distance around the earth at the Equator: _____

   b. The distance from the earth to the moon (center to center): _____

   c. The distance from the earth to the sun (center to center): _____

24. Models of the Solar System and the Universe

It is possible to make a scale model of the solar system (the sun and planets), but it requires a lot of space. Earth is one **astronomical unit** (1 AU) from the sun. An astronomical unit is 1.50×10^8 kilometers (9.3×10^6 miles). Neptune is 30 AU from the sun. Pluto lies nearly 40 AU from the sun. The sun's diameter (1.39×10^6 kilometers (864,000 miles)) is huge compared to the diameter of the planets. Earth's diameter, for example, is 13,000 kilometers (7,900 miles), less than 1/100 that of the sun. If we use a basketball, which is 24 cm (9.5 in) in diameter, to represent the sun, the Earth would be represented by a ball about 2.2 mm in diameter. On this scale, the centers of the basketball and ball would be 25 meters (84 feet) apart. Pluto (represented by an even tinier ball than Earth) would be nearly a kilometer from the basketball.

A scale model of the solar system sould be hard to make. What about a scale model of the universe?

Basically, the universe is made up of galaxies. These are large groupings of stars. There is even a structure to the galactal formations. As a first approximation, we can make two assumptions: first, that the galaxies are uniformly spread across the universe; and second, that the stars and their systems (such as the sun and its planets) are uniformly distributed in the galaxies.

The universe is estimated to be 10^{23} kilometers across. This estimate is made by examining the light from the most distant known galaxies. Analysis of this light indicates that it is 12–15 billion years old. Traveling at a speed of 3.0×10^5 km/s, it would have traveled:

$$15 \times 10^9 \text{ yr} \times 3.16 \times 10^7 \text{ s/yr} \times 3.0 \times 10^5 \text{ km/s} = 1.4 \times 10^{23} \text{ km}$$

Similar measurements indicate that galaxies have an average diameter of 10^{18} km. The galaxies themselves are separated by about 100 **galactal diameters** (10^{20} km).

Stars have an average diameter of 10^6 kilometers. They are roughly 100 million (10^8) star diameters (10^{14} km) apart.

If you are working in groups, the entire group can work on the three questions that follow. You will need to check one another as you fill in the table in question 1.

(continued)

24. Models of the Solar System and the Universe *(continued)*

1. This table contains information about our solar system. Fill in the blanks in the table.

The Sun and Planets						
Object	**Diameter (in km)**	**Relative diameter (Earth = 1.0)**	**Diameter of object in model**	**Radius of orbit (km)**	**Radius of orbit (A.U.)**	**Radius of orbit in model**
Sun	1.4×10^6	108	24 cm	NA	NA	NA
Mercury	5.2×10^3	0.38	0.8 mm	5.8×10^7	0.39	9.9 m
Venus	1.3×10^4	0.95	2.1 mm	1.1×10^8	0.73	____
Earth	1.3×10^4	1.0	2.2 mm	1.5×10^8	1.0	25 m
Mars	6.8×10^3	____	1.2 mm	2.3×10^8	1.53	____
Jupiter	1.4×10^5	10.8	____	7.8×10^8	____	130 m
Saturn	1.2×10^5	____	20 mm	1.4×10^9	9.3	____
Uranus	5.4×10^4	4.1	____	2.9×10^9	____	____
Neptune	5.0×10^4	____	8.4 mm	4.5×10^9	____	____
Pluto	6×106	0.2	____	5.9×109	39.3	985 m

NA means not applicable. The Sun's orbit is minimal in size.

2. As you have seen, it's difficult to show the solar system on any reasonable scale. And it is impossible to make a scale model of the universe. Draw a two-dimensional model or make a three-dimensional model of the universe recognizing that a scale model is impossible.

3. Astronomers see collisions of galaxies much more frequently than collisions of stars. Why do you think this might be?

25. Big Bang, Life, Dinosaurs, Humans, and a Time Line

Astronomers believe that the Big Bang (the beginning of the universe) took place about 2×10^{10} years ago. Our solar system began about 5×10^9 years ago. Living cells first existed in water about 3.5×10^9 years ago. Land animals appeared about 4×10^8 years ago and fossils of mammals go back about 2×10^8 years.

Dinosaurs first appeared 2.3×10^8 years ago. At that time, the earth had only one giant continent. About 150 million years ago, this large continent divided into two land masses called Laurasia and Godwana.

Approximately 1.0×10^8 years ago, Laurasia and Godwana broke into the five continents we have today. Until then, dinosaurs were spread all across the earth. The separation of the continents led to the development and separation of different species of dinosaurs on individual continents.

Recently, **paleontologists** (scientists who study fossils) found the fossils of two huge dinosaurs in Morocco. These fossils helped scientists determine that the five continents separated 100 million years ago.

One of the fossils was a gigantic 14-meter-long flesh-eating dinosaur. Named *Carcharodontosaurus saharicus*, this animal had a 1.62 meter-long head and sharp teeth. It roamed Morocco about 90 million years ago. *Carcharodontosaurus saharicus* was larger than *Tyrannosaurus rex*, which lived 70 million years ago. T-Rex was previously believed to be the largest flesh-eating animal that ever lived.

The second fossil discovery was a dinosaur completely new to science—*Deltadromeus agilis*. When this dinosaur lived, about 90 million years ago, the continents were well separated. This led to the isolation of dinosaurs and their evolution into very different species. Dinosaurs became extinct about 6.5×10^7 (65 million) years ago.

Primates (monkey-like creatures) have only been around for about 6×10^7 years. Primates believed to be the ancestors of humans lived about 2×10^6 years ago. Human-like fossils go back about 250,000 years. Neanderthal humans lived from about 100,000 to 40,000 years ago. Cro-Magnon were on earth about 60,000 years ago. Recorded human history is only 6,000 years old.

If you are working in groups, the entire group can work on the questions that follow. Once the time line is drawn, different people can work on the specific points in time asked for in the questions. Once all the marks are placed on the time line, the group should check the points to make sure they make sense. Finally, each person can do parts 2c and 2d and then compare results as a group.

(continued)

Name _____   Date _____

25. Big Bang, Life, Dinosaurs, Humans, and a Time Line *(continued)*

1. Draw a line one meter long on a sheet of paper. This line represents time, from the beginning of the universe until now. At the left end of the line, make a mark representing the beginning of the universe—the moment of the Big Bang. At the right end of the line, make a mark representing the present, 2×10^{10} years later. Since your time line contains 100 cm, each centimeter represents 2×10^{8} (200 million) years. On your time line, insert marks to show when each event took place.
   - our solar system began
   - the first living cells
   - the first land animals
   - the first mammals
   - the first dinosaurs
   - Laurasia and Godwana formed
   - Laurasia and Godwana broke into five continents
   - the dinosaur *Carcharodontosaurus saharicus* lived in Morocco
   - the dinosaur *Deltadromeus agilis* lived in Morocco
   - dinosaurs became extinct
   - the first primates
   - the appearance of primates believed to be the ancestors of humans
   - the appearance of the first humanlike animals
   - Neanderthals lived on the earth
   - Cro-Magnons lived on the earth
   - the beginning of recorded human history

2. In terms of the universe, humans appeared very recently. You probably found it hard to show the last 100,000 years on your time line. Make another time line one meter long to show the last two million years, during which humans evolved.

   a. On this new time line, what does one centimeter represent?

   b. On this new time line, insert marks to indicate:
      (1) the first primates believed to be the ancestors of humans
      (2) the appearance of the first human-like animals
      (3) the time that Neanderthals lived on the earth
      (4) the time that Cro-Magnons were on the earth
      (5) the beginning of recorded human history

   c. Consider Cro-Magnons to be humans. If you represent the age of the universe by one year, for how many seconds have humans been around? For how long have we been recording what we do? How long have you been around on this scale?

   d. If you represent the age of the universe by one day, for how many seconds have humans been here? For how long have we recorded what we do? How long have you been around on this scale?

                                       Middle School Math You Really Need

26. The Kuiper Belt

As long ago as 1951, the Dutch astronomer G.P. Kuiper had questions about our solar system. He suggested that it was really more complex than the well-accepted system of inner planets (Mercury, Venus, Earth and Mars), outer planets (Jupiter, Saturn, Uranus, Neptune and Pluto), and several hundred billion individual comets that make up the Oort belt. (This belt is between 3000 AU and 100,000 AU from the sun.)

The table below provides information about the planets found in our solar system. Remember, an astronomical unit—AU—is 1.50×10^2 km (9.3×10^6 miles).

The Planets

Planet	Radius of orbit (AU)	Diameter of planet (Earth = 1)
Mercury	0.39	0.38
Venus	0.723	0.95
Earth	1.0	1.0
Mars	1.52	0.53
Jupiter	5.2	11.3
Saturn	9.5	9.44
Uranus	19.2	4.10
Neptune	30.1	3.88
Pluto	39.4	0.2?

Pluto orbits the sun at 39.4 AU. More than 30 known bodies, up to 140 km in size (much smaller than planets), also orbit the sun at the same distance as Pluto. These objects, known as *Kuiper bodies*, have orbits that are in the same plane as Pluto's orbit. The plane of Pluto's orbit is different than the plane of the orbits of the other planets.

The Kuiper bodies, often called "short-period" comets, have elliptical, or oval, orbits. (The orbits of the planets are nearly circular.) The Kuiper bodies sometimes come closer to the earth than circular orbits would allow.

To date, more than 30 of these small short-period comets have been identified in the Kuiper belt. It is estimated that the Kuiper belt consists of at least 35,000 of these objects. Most are too far away to be detected.

(continued)

26. **The Kuiper Belt** *(continued)*

In 1987, J. X. Luu and D.C. Jewitt began a search for Kuiper bodies. They used a computer to generate pictures from the limited light entering the 2.2-meter telescope on Mauna Kea, Hawaii. Using a procedure called "blinking," astronomers can view images of Kuiper bodies and see that the bodies shift against a background of very distant, "fixed" stars—stars so far away that they show no motion over large periods of time. In 1992, they successfully proved the existence of the first of the Kuiper bodies, QB_1. This method has been used to find the 30 Kuiper bodies identified so far.

▼ ▼ ▼ ▼ ▼ ▼ ▼ ▼ ▼ ▼ ▼ ▼ ▼ ▼ ▼ ▼ ▼ ▼

If you are working in groups, divide into pairs. Do the three problems that follow with your partner. Then come back together as a group and compare your answers and solutions. Try to work out any differences you may have. Finally compare answers with other groups and resolve any differences.

▼ ▼ ▼ ▼ ▼ ▼ ▼ ▼ ▼ ▼ ▼ ▼ ▼ ▼ ▼ ▼ ▼ ▼

1. If you were to make a scale model of the entire solar system, including the Oort and the Kuiper belts, letting 1 centimeter equal 1 AU, how far from the sun would the Oort and Kuiper belts be found? What would their shapes be?

   Distance from sun to Oort belt: _____

   Distance from sun to Kuiper belt: _____

   Shape of Oort belt: _____

   Shape of Kuiper belt: _____

2. Where would the inner and the outer planets fit in this scaling?

   _____

   _____

   _____

3. How would the planetary bodies appear in size on this scale?

   _____

   _____

   _____

   _____

CHAPTER 5   **Math and Food**

To the Teacher

Anyone who goes food shopping, cooks, or tries to eat a healthy diet knows that food and numbers go together. The activities in this chapter should reinforce this fact for students. But they may not have realized that waiters as well as cooks have to use mathematics in their work.

27. *Nutritional Facts* (page 84)

Today, almost all processed foods have a label that provides information about the food and its nutritional content. Making intelligent use of this information requires a good deal of mathematics.

Here are some important conversion units for problem 7:

1 pound = 16 ounces

1 gallon = 4 quarts = 8 pints.

Answers

1. a. The can states that 250 mg is 10% of the DV. The daily requirement must be 10×250 mg , or 2500 mg .

    b. 2.5 grams

2. Tuna should not be a daily feature of this person's lunch, since three grams is already half a gram over the daily requirement. Salt is a substance which Americans should reduce in consumption.

3. These calculations were made on the basis of a 2000 calorie diet. For a 3000 calorie diet this would be only $\frac{2}{3}$ (2000/3000) of the requirement.

    a. cholesterol: $\frac{2}{3} \times 10\% = 6.7\%$

    b. protein: $\frac{2}{3}$ of $23\% = 15\%$

    c. fat: $\frac{2}{3} \times 8\% = 5.3\%$

    d. carbohydrate: $\frac{2}{3} \times 0\% = 0\%$

    e. daily caloric intake: 100/3000 = $0.033 = 3.3\%$

4. The daily requirement of protein is 13/ 0.23 = 57 grams. ($0.23 \times$ (requirement) = 13 grams). Since tuna packed in oil yields 16 g of protein per serving, this is $16/57 \times 100 = 28\%$ of the daily requirement.

5. a. $23\% \times 3/2 = 35\%$

    b. $190 \times 3/2 = 285$ calories

    c. $5\% = 1/20; 20 \times 120 = 2400$ mg = 2.4 g

    d. 20 servings $\times$ 2 tablespoons/serving = 40 tablespoons

    e. Two tablespoons contains 23% or about $\frac{1}{4}$ of the DV total fat. So 4 $\times$ 2 tablespoons = 8 tablespoons. A more exact calculation would be:

    $1 \div 0.23 = 4.35; 4.35 \times 2$ tablespoons = 8.7 tablespoons

28. *Milk, Lowfat Milk, and Skim Milk* (page 86)

This section focuses on one food item—milk! Students might like to extend this section to include milk products richer in fat, such as half and half, cream, and whipping cream.

Answers

1.

Serving size = 1 cup (236 mL)	2% milk
Servings per container	16
	Amounts per serving
	236 mL
Calories (total)	130
Calories from fat	46
	(weight and/or % of Daily Value)
Total fat	5 g (8%)
Saturated fat	3 g (15%)
Cholesterol	20 mg (7%)
Sodium	125 mg (5%)
Total carbohydrate	12 g (4%)
Dietary fiber	0 g (0%)
Sugars	12 g
Protein	8 g (17%)
Vitamin A	10%
Vitamin C	4%
Calcium	30%
Iron	0%
Vitamin D	25%

2. For the skim, 1%, and 2%: 16×236 mL = 3776 mL, 3.776 L, or 1 gallon. For the whole milk: 4×236 mL = 944 mL, 0.944 L or 1 quart.

3. a. 4 cups/q̶t̶ $\times$ 4 q̶t̶/gal = 16 cups/gal

   b. 8 oz/c̶u̶p̶ $\times$ 16 c̶u̶p̶/gal = 128 oz/gal

      128 oz/gal $\times$ 1 gal/4 qt = 32 oz/qt

   c. 236 mL/c̶u̶p̶ $\div$ 8 oz/c̶u̶p̶ = 29.5 mL/oz

   d. 236 mL/c̶u̶p̶ $\times$ 16 c̶u̶p̶/gal = 3776 mL/gal

4. 236 m̶L̶/serving $\times$ 1.03 g/m̶L̶ = 243 g/serving

   2.5 g $\div$ 243 g = 0.0102; 0.0102 $\times$ 100 = 0.99%

5. 8 g $\div$ 243 g = 0.033; 0.033 $\times$ 100 = 3.3%

6. a. –e.: the percentage of fat has no effect.

   f. Doubling the fat content doubles the cholesterol content.

7. a. 10%/cup $\times$? = 100%; ? = 10 cups.

   b. 4%/cup $\times$? = 100%; ? = 25 cups.

   c. 25%/cup $\times$? = 100%; ? = 4 cups.

   d. 30%/cup $\times$? = 100%; ? = 3.3 cups.

8. 6%/cup $\times$? = 100%; ? = 100% $\div$ 6%/up = 17 cups

9. About 6/10. 1.5 g $\div$ 2.5 g = 0.6; 3 g $\div$ 5 g = 0.6; 5 g $\div$ 8 g = 0.63

29. *Math at the Grocery Store* (page 89)

This activity could be done as a homework assignment. You could assign different food items to different students or student groups. You might then collect and evaluate their findings or have them report the results of their investigations to the entire class. In that way the class can share and compare information for different items from different stores.

Be sure that the items compared are exactly the same in all respects except the quantity packaged.

Answers

Answers will depend on the items investigated and their prices per unit volume or weight. Generally, students will find that the price per unit measure decreases as the size of the package increases. This makes sense because packaging costs per unit volume or weight increase as the package grows smaller. It costs a lot more to pack 16 ounces of cereal into eight 2-ounce boxes than to put it all in one 16-ounce box.

Here is an example that compares identical brands of tomato puree.

Net weight (oz.)	Cost (¢)	¢/oz.
29	150	5.2
15	80	5.3
6	40	6.7

The larger size cans are less costly. This is not always true, however.

30. *Serving Food* (page 91)

This is another example showing that math is needed in almost any occupation. You might extend the lesson by providing a menu and asking students to determine how much silverware will be needed for the banquet.

Answers

1. 225 – 12 = 213; 213/8 = 26.6; 27 round tables will be needed.

2. 27 tables ÷ 2 tables/waiter = 13.5 waiters. You can either hire 13 waiters and ask one experienced waiter to serve three tables or use an apprentice waiter who will serve only one table and help you bus dishes at the head table.

3. 225/12 = 18.75; 19 trays will be needed, but one tray will have only 9 salads.

4. 225 desserts ÷ 15 trays = 15 desserts/ tray.

27. Nutritional Facts

Below is a reprint of the "Nutrition Facts" found on the back of a can of solid white tuna in water. Most commercially packaged foods today have similar statements about their nutritional content. How does one go about using this information?

Nutritional Facts

Serving size: 2 oz. drained (56 grams/about $\frac{1}{4}$ cup)

calories: 100   fat cal: 45

Percent daily values (DV) are based on a 2000 calorie diet.

amount per serving	% DV	amount per serving	% DV
total fat 5 g	8%	carbohydrates 0 g	0%
saturated fat 2 g	10%	fiber 0 g	
cholesterol 30 mg	10%	sugars 0 g	0%
sodium 250 mg	10%	protein 13 g	23%

Vitamin A 0% • Vitamin C 0% • Calcium 0% • Iron 0% • Niacin 25% • Vitamin B-6 10% •Vitamin B-12 15% • phosphorus 10%

This can was labeled: "Contents: 9 oz, 255 grams. Servings: about 4."

▼ ▼ ▼ ▼ ▼ ▼ ▼ ▼ ▼ ▼ ▼ ▼ ▼ ▼ ▼ ▼ ▼ ▼

If you work in groups, divide into pairs. Each of you should do the following problems by yourselves. Then compare answers with your partner and resolve any differences. Finally, meet in the larger group to compare answers and solutions and discuss any differences that may exist.

▼ ▼ ▼ ▼ ▼ ▼ ▼ ▼ ▼ ▼ ▼ ▼ ▼ ▼ ▼ ▼ ▼ ▼

1. The daily value (DV) means the amount you should eat every day—the daily requirement.

   a. Based on the information above, what is the daily requirement, in milligram (mg), for sodium? _____

   b. A milligram is 1/1000 (0.001) gram. What is the daily requirement in grams?

(continued)

27. **Nutritional Facts** *(continued)*

2. If a person already gets 3 grams of sodium per day from other foods (bacon, chipped beef, pickled fish, etc.), should he or she include a serving of tuna with every lunch? Why? _____

3. A teenager's usual daily caloric intake is about 3000 calories. Decide what percent of DV a serving of tuna will provide for a teenager for each of the following:

   a. cholesterol _____

   b. protein _____

   c. fat _____

   d. carbohydrate _____

   e. daily caloric intake _____

4. Tuna packed in oil contains 16 grams of protein per 2 oz serving. What percent of the daily protein requirement is this for a 2000 calorie daily diet?

5. The label on a jar of peanut butter states that 2 tablespoons (30 g) is a serving. It tells us, too, that one serving contains 190 calories and 23% DV total fat. The sodium content per serving is 120 mg (5% DV).

   a. If someone ate 3 tablespoons of peanut butter, what percent DV in total fat would that be? _____

   b. How many calories were in the peanut butter the person ate?

   _____

   c. According to the label, what is the DV of sodium in milligrams and in grams?

   d. How many tablespoons of peanut butter would you have to eat to reach the DV for sodium? _____

   e. How many tablespoons of peanut butter would you have to eat to reach the DV for total fat? _____

28. Milk, Lowfat Milk, and Skim Milk

Half a century ago, milk came in clear one-quart bottles. You could see the cream (the fatty part of the milk) at the top of the bottle. The cream had a yellowish tinge. Because it was less dense than the rest of the milk, it would float on the whiter milk in the lower part of the bottle. If you wanted milk with less fat, you could pour off the cream.

Today most milk comes in quart, half-gallon, or gallon containers made of plastic or cardboard. You can buy whole milk, which still has the cream in it, skim milk, from which the cream has been removed, or milk from which some of the cream has been removed. You don't see the cream in milk because it has been broken into tiny particles that stay suspended in the rest of the milk. We say it has been homogenized.

The table below lists four kinds of milk available in most stores—skim, 1%, 2%, and whole milk. The table also shows the information found in the Nutrition Facts labels on the containers in which these different kinds of milk are sold. The values listed as calories, grams (g) or percent (%) are amounts per serving.

Serving size= 1 cup (236 mL)	skim milk	1% milk	2% milk	whole milk
Servings per container	16	16	16	4
	Amounts per serving			
	236 mL	236 mL	_____	236 mL
Calories (total)	90	110	_____	150
Calories from fat	0	23	_____	70
	(weight and/or % of Daily Value)			
Total fat	0 g (0%)	2.5 g (4%)	_____	8 g(12%)
Saturated fat	0 g (0%)	1.5 g (8%)	_____	5 g (25%)
Cholesterol	< 5 mg (1%)	10 mg(4%)	_____	35 mg (11%)
Sodium	125 mg(5%)	125 mg (5%)	_____	125 mg (5%)
Total carbohydrate	13 g (4%)	12 g (4%)	_____	12 g (4%)

(continued)

28. Milk, Lowfat Milk, and Skim Milk (continued)

Serving size= 1 cup (236 mL)	skim milk	1% milk	2% milk	whole milk
Dietary fiber	0 g (0%)	0 g (0%)	_____	0 g (0%)
Sugars	12 g	12 g	_____	12 g
Protein	8 g (17%)	8 g (17%)	_____	8 g (17%)
Vitamin A	10%	10%	_____	10%
Vitamin C	4%	4%	_____	4%
Calcium	30%	30%	_____	30%
Iron	0%	0%	_____	0%
Vitamin D	25%	25%	_____	25%

▼ ▼ ▼ ▼ ▼ ▼ ▼ ▼ ▼ ▼ ▼ ▼ ▼ ▼ ▼ ▼ ▼ ▼

If you work in groups, divide into pairs. Work together on question 1. Then do questions 2–9 by yourself. Once you have completed the problems, compare answers with your partner. Finally, meet as a larger group to compare and discuss answers, solutions, and any differences that may exist.

▼ ▼ ▼ ▼ ▼ ▼ ▼ ▼ ▼ ▼ ▼ ▼ ▼ ▼ ▼ ▼ ▼ ▼

1. Use the information about other types of milk to work out how to fill in the spaces in the table under 2% milk.

2. Based on the serving size and the number of servings per container, what is the size of the containers listed in the table?

   skim milk _____
   1% milk _____
   2% milk _____
   whole milk _____

3. A cup is 1/4 quart or 8 ounces and a gallon is 4 quarts. A liter (L) is 1,000 mL. Using the information in the chart, convert the following measurements.

   a. How many cups are there in a gallon? _____

   b. How many ounces are there in a gallon? _____ In a quart? _____

(continued)

28. Milk, Lowfat Milk, and Skim Milk (continued)

    c. How many milliliters (mL) in an ounce? _____

    d. How many milliliters (mL) are there in a gallon? _____

4. One percent (1%) milk is supposed to be only 1% fat. Based on the total fat per serving for 1% milk given in the table, confirm that the milk really is 1% fat. You may assume that a milliliter (mL) of milk weighs 1.03 gram (g).

5. Milk that has not had any fat removed is supposed to be at least 3.25% fat. Confirm that the homogenized whole milk in the table meets this requirement.

6. What effect does the percentage of fat in milk have on the milk's:

    a. sodium content _____

    b. sugar content _____

    c. protein content _____

    d. fiber content _____

    e. calcium and iron content _____

    f. cholesterol content _____

7. How much milk should you drink each day to obtain your daily requirement of:

    a. vitamin A _____

    b. vitamin C _____

    c. vitamin D _____

    d. calcium _____

8. The milk shown in the table has been enriched with extra vitamin A. A carton of milk with no added vitamins lists the percent of daily value per serving as 6% for vitamin A. How many glasses of this milk would you have to drink each day to meet your vitamin A requirement? _____

9. What fraction of the fat in milk is saturated fat? _____

29. Math at the Grocery Store

It is really helpful to take a small hand calculator with you when you go grocery shopping. In that way you can find the cost per unit measure of the groceries you buy. Cost per unit measure can be expressed as cents per ounce (¢/oz), dollars per pound ($/lb), cents per pint (¢/pt), or any other measure of cost per weight or volume.

Buying large rather than small quantities is often less expensive if you consider the cost per unit measure. To figure out the most economical way to buy, you should calculate the cost per unit measure. This can often be done by reading the price tags posted under the item.

If the cost per unit measure is not given, how can you tell which of two items is the best buy? Find the units in which the item is measured—ounces, pounds, grams, etc. Then divided the item's price by the number of units it contains. This will tell you how much each unit costs. For example, take a 10-ounce box of cereal that costs $2.99.

$$2.99 \div 10 = .29$$

Each ounce of cereal costs 29¢.

If you work in groups, go to a grocery store with a partner if possible. Then meet in a larger group to compare results. Your teacher may ask the groups to meet as a full class to share results for different products and stores.

Go to a grocery store and find several products that are sold in different sizes. Be sure that each item is identical in every way except size—same maker, description, nutrition facts, etc. Canned goods and breakfast cereals are good items to use.

Calculate the cost per unit measure of each item. Can you reach any conclusion regarding cost per unit measure? Why do you think cost per unit measure varies as the size of the package changes?

(continued)

29. Math at the Grocery Store (continued)

Item 1

Size: _____

Total cost of the item: _____

Cost per unit measure: _____

Item 2

Size: _____

Total cost of the item: _____

Cost per unit measure: _____

Item 1

Size: _____

Total cost of the item: _____

Cost per unit measure: _____

30. Serving Food

You are the head waiter at a restaurant. Tonight the restaurant will prepare and serve a banquet for 225 people.

If you work in groups, divide into pairs. Each of you should do the following 4 problems by yourselves. Then compare answers with your partner and resolve any differences. Finally, the group can come back together to compare answers and discuss any differences.

1. Twelve people will be seated at the head table. The rest of the guests will be seated at round tables. Eight chairs can be placed comfortably around a single round table. How many round tables will be needed for the banquet?

   _____

2. As head waiter, you will serve the head table. Each other waiter will serve two round tables. How many waiters, other than yourself, will be needed?

   _____

3. In order to provide prompt service, the salads will be prepared ahead of time and placed on trays. Twelve salad plates will fit on a tray. How many trays will be needed for the salads?

   _____

4. The desserts will also be placed on trays while people eat the main course. Each tray can hold 15 dessert plates. How many trays will be needed for the desserts?

   _____

CHAPTER 6   Math in Many Places

To the Teacher

As the title of this chapter implies, we find uses for mathematics in many places. Perhaps one of the greatest uses of math is in making estimates and approximations, a topic that is far too often ignored in schools, but one that is of great value in everyday life. In addition to estimating and approximating, students will see how math is used in measuring property, scaling, finding speeds from distances and times, and using a light meter. They will also see that negative numbers are used in the real world, that a hand calculator can be used to find the value of numbers raised to large powers, as happens with interest rates and that prime numbers can be fun even if they are not very useful.

31. *Estimating and Approximating*
(page 100)

Students are usually hesitant about making estimations or approximations, especially in a math class where they think there must be a "right" answer. It is important to encourage them to make estimates and approximations. It's an ability that is really needed; the sooner it is acquired, the better.

The class will need several measuring tapes to measure the distance covered by 50 paces. You might avoid this need by having a starting line and another line approximately 50 student paces beyond it. Students could then compare their 50 paces to a standard distance, such as 250 feet, and add or subtract the difference between their 50 paces and the standard to find the distance they walked.

Students will need balances, gravel, and measuring cups for question 6. You might reduce the amount of equipment needed by weighing one cup of gravel as a class demonstration.

Additional examples of the use of estimating and approximating can be found in Operating Costs of Electrical Appliances in Chapter 3.

Answers

The answers to all these questions will vary. They are estimates, not exact measurements.

1. Answers will vary. If a school has 35 classrooms with an average of 30 students per class, the school has approximately $35 \times 30 = 1050$ students. The registrar might give 1012 as the actual count, which is 38 less than the estimate. So the estimate is $(38 \div 1012) \times 100 = 3.8\%$ more than the actual number.

2. The length of a pace can be calculated by dividing the distance walked by the 100 paces taken. A student might pace off 490 feet in 100 paces. Then the length of a pace is $490 \div 100 = 4.9$ ft/pace.

3. Answers will vary.

4. A baseball diamond is really a square, 90 × 90 feet, so the area = 90 ft × 90 ft = 8100 sq ft. If an athletic field is used, answers will vary depending on the field used.

5. Answers will vary.

6. a. The mass of 8 oz of paving gravel will depend on the gravel chosen. An example might be 420 grams. Since a pound contains 454 grams, the weight in pounds is 420 g ÷ 454 g/lb = 0.93 lb.

   b. Since there are approximately 14 cubic inches in 8 ounces, each cubic inch weighs 0.93 lb ÷ 14 in^3 = 0.066 lb. A cubic foot would weigh 1728 times as much because there are 1728 cubic inches in a cubic foot. 0.066 lb × 1728 = 114 lb or 114 lb × 454 g/lb = 51,756 g or 51.8 kg.

   c. A cubic yard contains 27 cubic feet. Based on the weight of gravel presumed for an 8 ounce cup, a cubic yard would weigh 27 times as much as a cubic foot or 27 × 114 lb = 3,078 lb or 1400 kg.

7. An estimate for the volume of a truckload of gravel might measure 14 ft × 10 ft × 6 ft = 840 cu ft = 840 cu ft ÷ 27 cu ft/cu yd = 31 cu yd.

8. a. 31 cu yd × 3,078 lb/cu yd = 95,000 lb.

   b. 95,000 lb ÷ 2.2 lb/kg = 43,000 kg.

   c. 95,000 lb ÷ 2,000 lb/ton = 47.5 tons.

32. *Math and Property* (page 102)

Depending on where you live, land may be more commonly measured in square feet or acres. A century ago, the rod was a more common unit of measurement. It is included here for its historical value and because it provides more practice with unit conversions

— something we all need to deal with throughout our lives.

Answers

1. 16.5 ft/rd ÷ 3 ft/yd = 5.5 yd/rd

2. 5.5 yd/rd × 5.5 yd/rd = 30.25 sq yd/sq rd

3. 160 sq rd/acre × 30.25 sq yd/sq rd = 4840 sq yd/acre

4. 5280 ft/mi ÷ 16.5 ft/rd = 320 rd/mi

5. 150 ft × 140 ft = 21,000 sq ft = 0.48 acre. Although the land is slightly less than half an acre, most towns will consider it an acceptable building lot in areas zoned for 0.5 acre lots.

6. Answers will vary, but all lots should be 1.0 acre or 43,560 sq ft.

7. a. 100 ft. × 120 ft. = 12,000 sq ft
   $$\frac{12,000 \text{ sq ft}}{43,560 \text{ sq ft/acre}} = 0.28 \text{ acre.}$$

   b. 200 ft × 60 ft = 12,000 sq ft = 0.28 acre

   c. 100 ft × 125 ft = 12,500 sq ft
   $$\frac{12,500 \text{ sq ft}}{43,560 \text{ sq ft/acre}} = 0.29 \text{ acre}$$

   d. 137 ft × 100 ft = 13,500 sq ft
   $$\frac{13,500 \text{ sq ft}}{43,560 \text{ sq ft/acre}} = 0.31 \text{ acre}$$

   e. 140 ft. × 100 ft. = 14,000 sq ft
   $$\frac{14,000 \text{ sq ft}}{43,560 \text{ sq ft/acre}} = 0.32 \text{ acre}$$

   f. 200 ft × 100 ft = 20,000 sq ft
   $$\frac{20,000 \text{ sq ft}}{43,560 \text{ sq ft/acre}} = 0.46 \text{ acre}$$

   g. 130 ft × 80 ft = 10,400 sq ft
   $$\frac{10,400 \text{ sq ft}}{43,560 \text{ sq ft/acre}} = 0.24 \text{ acre}$$

   h. (60 ft × 200 ft) + (70 ft × 80 ft) = 17,600 sq ft

$$\frac{17,600 \text{ sq ft}}{43,560 \text{ sq ft/acre}} = 0.40 \text{ acre}$$

  i. 100 ft × 200 = 20,000 sq ft

$$\frac{20,000 \text{ sq ft}}{43,560 \text{ sq ft/acre}} = 0.46 \text{ acre}$$

  j. (75 ft × 120 ft) + [(80 + 60 + 100 + 62 − 100 − 75)ft.] × 120 ft/2 = 16,500 sq ft

$$\frac{16,500 \text{ sq ft}}{43,560 \text{ sq ft/acre}} = 0.38 \text{ acre}$$

8. a. 160 ~~acres~~ × 43,560 sq ft/~~acre~~ = 6,969,600 sq ft

  b. Use the square root key to find the square root of 6,969,600 sq ft.

  c. 2640 ft

  d. 2640 ft ÷ 5280 ft/mi = 0.5 mi

  e. 0.5 mi × 0.5 mi = 0.25 sq mi

  f. As shown in Figure T6.1, a square mile would contain four 0.25 square mile plots or 4 × 160 acres = 640 acres. Since each settler was to get 160 acres, four settlers could occupy the square mile plot of land.

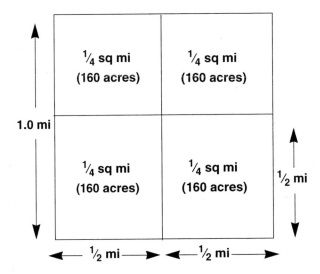

Figure T6.1 A square mile contains 640 acres

33. *Prime Numbers* (page 106)

Prime numbers are of great interest and use to mathematicians, but they have no real, everyday use. They are included here only because they are fun to think about.

Answers

1. The prime numbers between 38 and 101 are 41, 43, 47, 53, 59, 61, 67, 71, 73, 79, 83, 89, 91, and 97.

2. The twin prime numbers from 5 to 38 are 5 and 7, 11 and 13, 17 and 19, 29 and 31.

3. The numbers that lie between the twin prime numbers listed above are 6, 12, 18 and 30.

4. The numbers listed in question 3 are multiples of both 2 and 3.

5. The twin prime numbers between 38 and 110 are 41 and 43, 59 and 61, 71 and 73, 89 and 91, 101 and 103, 107 and 109.

6. The numbers that lie between the twin prime numbers listed in question 5 are 42, 60, 72, 90, 102 and 108.

7. The numbers listed in question 6 are multiples of both 2 and 3.

8. a. 2 is a prime number because it has no factors other than itself and one.

  b. 2 is the only even prime number because any other even number is divisible by at least 2, itself and one, meaning it has more than two factors.

9. a. 5 is a prime number because it has no factors other than itself and one.

  b. Any other number ending in 5, such as 15, 25, 35, . . . cannot be a prime number because it would be divisible by 5, itself and one, meaning it has more than two factors.

10. a. Prime numbers from 5 to 101 are 5, 7, 11, 13, 17, 19, 23, 29, 31, 37, 41, 43, 47, 53, 59, 61, 67, 71, 73, 79, 83, 89, 91, 97 and 101.

When increased <u>or</u> decreased by 1, they are divisible by 6:

6, 6, 12, 12, 18, 18, 24, 30, 30, 36, 42, 42, 48, 54, 60, 60, 66, 72, 72, 78, 84, 90, 96 and 102.

  b. Some prime numbers greater than 101 are 103, 107, 109, 113, 127, . . .

When increased <u>or</u> decreased by 1, we get 102, 108, 114, 126, . . . These numbers are all divisible by 6.

  c. This rule does not apply to prime numbers less than five, since a number less than 5 cannot be evenly divisible by 6.

11. All prime numbers with 2 or more digits ending in an even digit (0, 2, 4, 6 or 8) are divisible by 2, and so are not prime. All numbers ending in 5 are divisible by 5, and so are not prime. This leaves 1, 3, 7 and 9 as the only possible ending digits for prime numbers of two or more digits.

34. Scaling *(page 108)*

These questions are statements with missing words. Students are expected to find a number suggested by the statement and a comparable matching number with suitable units such as a distance, time, or population density.

Answers

1. "If the United States' 1990 national deficit of 220.469 billion dollars were to be laid out dollar by dollar, it would stretch from here to . . ."

$220,469,000,000 \times 6$ in/$ $= 1.32 \times 10^{12}$ inches

1.0 mile contains 12 in/ft $\times$ 5280 ft/mi = 63,360 in;

1.32×10^{12} inches $\div 6.336 \times 10^{4}$ in/mi = 2.1×10^{7} miles

This is about 21 million miles, about 840 times around the earth's equator, about 87 round trips to the Moon, or whatever reasonable statements students come up with.

2. The earth is 8000 mi in diameter and the sun is 1,000,0000 mi in diameter or 125 $\times$ as wide. An orange has a diameter of about 3 inches; therefore, the sun's diameter would be:

3 inches $\times$ (1,000,000 $\div$ 8000) = 375 inches = 31.25 feet.

So the sun might be a house or anything about 30 feet in length, width, and height.

3. The distance from New York to Los Angeles is 2466 miles, and New York to Chicago is 727 mi.

Therefore, 1 hour $\times$ (727 $\div$ 2466) = 0.3 hour, or 18 minutes.

4. Belgium's area is 11,781 square miles and India's is 1,269,339 square miles. The population of Belgium is 10,000,000 and that of India is 685,000,000. If all of India's people were placed in Belgium, its population density would become:

10 million + 685 million $\div$ 11,781 square miles = 59,000 people/sq mi instead of 849 people/sq mi. Thus, its population density would rise by almost 70 times.

35. Velocity from Distance and Time *(page 109)*

Questions 1 and 2 involve work that can be done in the classroom. Question 3 is an activity in which students can make measurements of distance and time to determine the velocity of vehicles, bicycles, and pedestrians. If there is a road near the school where such measurements can be taken, you might like to have students carry out the activity in pairs or small groups. The activity can also be done as a homework assignment, but parents should be notified to ensure that students work safely. There is no need for them to be close to the road to make the measurements.

Answers

1. 1 mi/1.13 min = 0.88 mi/min

   0.88 mi/min × 60 min/h = 53 mph

2. a. 30 mi/28.2 min × 60 min/h = 64 mph

   b. 30 mi/50.2 min × 60 min/h = 36 mph

   c. The high speed in part a would suggest the car was traveling on a superhighway. The speed in part b would suggest a secondary, winding, narrow or otherwise restricting road.

3. a. Quite likely some vehicles will exceed the speed limit.

   b. Yes. The speed of pedestrians will be significantly less than the speed of cars. Depending on the road chosen, cyclists' speeds may be significantly less or similar to the speed of motor vehicles.

   c. The two speeds should be reasonably close to each other.

36. Are Negative Numbers Ever Real? *(page 112)*

Negative numbers are all too real. Students will realize this when they have their own checking accounts, but they often find the idea of negative numbers baffling. To help remove the mystery, we begin with negative temperatures—something that students who live where the winters are cold can readily relate to.

Answers

1. –28 °C

2. –40°F

3.

Paris Noon Temperature	New York Report
20°C	68°F
35°C	95°F
–10°C	14°F
12°C	54°F
5°C	41°F
–5°C	23°F

4.

Dallas noon Temperature	Rome Report
80°F	27°C
35°F	2°C
–10°F	–23°C
102°F	39°C
12°F	–11°C
–25°F	–32°C

5. Assets: cash on hand $1,000,000 + bank savings account $32,000,000 = $33,000,000. Debts: outstanding bills $2,000,000 + salaries due $ 1,500,000 + unpaid bills $3,500,000 = $7,000,000

   Net worth = $33 million – 7 million = $26 million.

37. Handheld Calculators *(page 114)*

Students will need calculators with a y^x key for these activities.

This section deals with the function y^x. Students usually know how to use the addition, subtraction, multiplication and division functions on a handheld calculator, and functions like square root and percentage are easily learned. However, the y^x function is not an easy one for students, but once understood they will find it very useful.

You may want students to review simple and compound interest in Chapter 3 before and after they do this section.

Answers

Using the calculator:

1. $12^3 = 1728$
2. $2^5 = 32$
3. $4^6 = 4096$
4. $3.14^5 = 305$
5. $12^{3.1} = 2215$
6. $2.01^{5.02} = 33.3$
7. $1.54^{17.7} = 2085$
8. $7.54^{4.2376} = 5223$
9. $S = P(1 + r)^t$. Here P = \$10,000, r = 4.65%, and t = 10 years.
   $S = P(1 + r)^t = \$10,000 (1 + .0465)^{10} = \$15,754$
10. Once again, $S = P(1 + r)^t = \$18,000 (1 + r)^t$. Here rate, r = 4.0/4 = 1.0% and t = 14 (quarters). Therefore, $S = P(1 + r)^t = \$18,000(1 + 0.01)^{14} = \$18,000(1.149) = \$20,691$.

38. Photographic Light Meters
(page 116)

Anyone attempting to learn photography will need to understand shutter speed, aperture, film speed, and subject illumination. Automatic cameras are fine for snapshots, but they are not satisfactory when more serious work is to be done.

There are many kinds of handheld light meters. However, they all work on the same basic principles: the relationships between aperture, film speed, and shutter speed.

In teaching this unit, it would be helpful for each student to have a handheld meter. However, even having one that you can show the class will make it possible for students to see how the various rotating dials are interconnected. Without a meter, you will have to do a lot of explaining of Figure 6.8.

Explaining the exact meaning of f-number is probably too difficult, but the fact that bigger f-numbers mean smaller apertures must be accepted or demonstrated, as must the halving of the aperture sizes as we go from f/1.4 to f/2, to f/2.8, . . . to f/22 and to f/32. The order of these f-numbers must be memorized!

Actually, the f-number is inversely proportional to the area of the aperture and to the square of the diameter of the aperture.

Answers

1. The speed, 1/500 s, lies halfway between f-numbers 5.6 and 8.
2. The film speed ASA 250 is twice as "fast" as ASA 125. This means the camera and film are twice as receptive to the light coming from the subject as the ASA 125 film. For the same light exposure, the shutter will have to admit half as much light. Half of 1/100 s at f/16 is 1/200 s at f/16.
3. At 1/100 s, instead of the original 1/50 s, we have halved the time of exposure, in other words, we have halved the amount of light striking the film. We need to double the exposure to get back to the original meter reading of

light intensity, and then double it again to double that exposure. So altogether we must quadruple the opening of the aperture. We must go from f/11 to f/8 to double the aperture opening, and then from f/8 to f/5.6 to double it again.

4. A film with speed ASA 1000 is eight times as sensitive to light intensity as ASA 125 (1000/125 = 8). We will need to cut the light admitted by a factor of eight (not considering the change from f/22 to f/16).

   A photo taken on ASA 125 film shows a light intensity of 1/50 at f/22. (See the setting on Figure 6.8.) Going from f/22 to f/16 doubles the aperture opening, and means we must halve the light admitted to the camera. These two effects together mean that we must cut the indicated exposure by $8 \times 2 = 16$. If 1/50 s is divided by 16 we get 0.00125 s, or 1/800 s.

   You can demonstrate this with a meter. Change the film speed indicator from ASA 125 to ASA 1000. Read the shutter time at f/16 instead of f/22. It will read 1/800 s. (Or, using Figure 6.8, notice that we can get an equivalent exposure at 1/100 s, f/16. Because our film is eight times more sensitive, we only need $1/8 \times 1/100$ s. = 1/800 s shutter speed.)

5. If the intensity of illumination should read 400 instead of the 200 shown in the photo, the scales would all be shifted one space clockwise. The shutter speed for f/16 would be 1/250 s.

31. Estimating and Approximating

It is often helpful to estimate or approximate the answer to a problem or calculation. Sometimes you don't need an exact answer. And sometimes your estimate can help you tell if your calculations are right.

▼ ▼ ▼ ▼ ▼ ▼ ▼ ▼ ▼ ▼ ▼ ▼ ▼ ▼ ▼ ▼ ▼ ▼ ▼

If you are working in groups, divide into pairs. Each pair can then work together to find answers for the questions that follow. Then gather in groups of four to compare your answers and work out any differences you may have. Remember these are estimates. All you can expect is that the estimates be reasonable. For questions 6 and 7, a lot will depend on the weight you find for a cup of gravel.

▼ ▼ ▼ ▼ ▼ ▼ ▼ ▼ ▼ ▼ ▼ ▼ ▼ ▼ ▼ ▼ ▼ ▼ ▼

1. Find out how many classrooms are being used in your school. Then estimate the average number of students in a class. Use these two pieces of information to find the approximate number of students in your school. How does your approximation compare with the exact census given by your school's registrar? By what percentage did your approximation differ from the actual enrollment?

   Estimate: _____ Actual: _____ Difference (%): _____

2. It is useful to be able to approximate a distance. Suppose you want to measure off a baseball diamond or lines for a 100-yard dash. You don't need these measurements to the nearest inch, but you would like them to the nearest foot. You can easily lay out the field or measure the dash distance if you know the length of your pace. A pace is sketched in Figure 6.1.

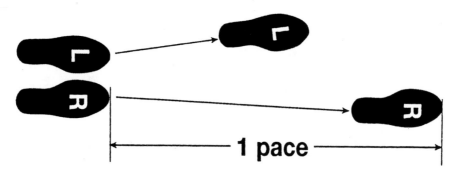

Figure 6.1   A pace consists of two steps. What's the length of your pace?

(continued)

31. **Estimating and Approximating** *(continued)*

When you walk, every time your right foot goes down you have covered another pace. Measure the distance covered by 100 of your paces. How can you use that measurement to find the length of your pace? What is the average length of one of your paces?

Pace length _____

3. Now find the number of paces that will take you from one block to the next, or from one lamp post or telephone pole to the next. Knowing the length of one of your paces, find the length of a block, the distance from post to post or pole to pole.

4. Find the area of a baseball diamond or an athletic field using paces to measure lengths.

5. Think of a verbal method of estimating seconds. For example, you can say, "one-potato, two-potato, three-potato, . . . " Now see how accurately you can use your method to estimate a minute. Have a partner with a wristwatch or clock that has a second hand check the time to compare your estimate with actual time. Was your estimate of a minute too long or too short? By what percentage did your estimate differ from a true minute?

6. Weigh gravel in a measuring cup. Fill it to the 8-ounce line. An 8-ounce cup contains about 14 cubic inches.

   a. How much does the gravel weigh? _____

   b. Estimate the weight of a cubic foot of gravel. _____

   c. Estimate the weight of a cubic yard of gravel. _____

7. Estimate the volume of a truckload of gravel.

8. Estimate the weight of a truckload of gravel:

   a. in pounds _____

   b. in kilograms _____

   c. in tons _____

32. Math and Property

Someday you may want to buy property. Before you do, you should know how land is measured and sold.

Traditionally, land in the United States has been measured in acres. An acre of land contains 160 square rods (sq rd). A rod is 16.5 feet long. A square rod (Figure 6.2) covers an area that is 16.5 feet long and 16.5 feet wide or 272.25 square feet (sq ft). Since an acre of land covers 160 square rods, its area is equal to:

160 sq rd × 272.25 sq ft/sq rd = 43,560 sq ft = 1.0000 acre

Although the rod is the basis of the acre, the rod itself is no longer used as a unit of measure.

As you can see from Figure 6.3, an acre can have various shapes. But all the shapes cover the same area — 1 acre, 160 sq rd or 43,560 sq ft. Today, building lots are often measured in square feet, particularly when the lots are less than one acre in area.

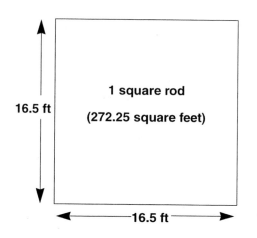

Figure 6.2   A square rod contains 272.25 square feet.

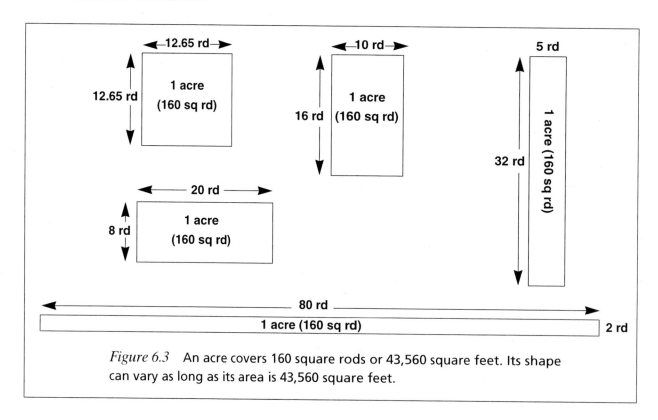

Figure 6.3   An acre covers 160 square rods or 43,560 square feet. Its shape can vary as long as its area is 43,560 square feet.

(continued)

Name _____ Date _____

32. Math and Property *(continued)*

▼ ▼ ▼ ▼ ▼ ▼ ▼ ▼ ▼ ▼ ▼ ▼ ▼ ▼ ▼ ▼ ▼ ▼

If you are working in groups, divide into pairs. Each individual can then work on the first 5 questions and compare answers. Then gather in your larger group to compare your answers and work out any differences you may have. Once you reach agreement, the entire group can work on questions 6, 7, and 8. Then meet with another group to compare and review your answers.

▼ ▼ ▼ ▼ ▼ ▼ ▼ ▼ ▼ ▼ ▼ ▼ ▼ ▼ ▼ ▼ ▼ ▼

1. How many yards are there in one rod? _____

2. How many square yards are there in one square rod? _____

3. How many square yards are there in an acre? _____

4. How many rods are equal to one mile? _____

5. A realtor shows you a map of a building lot (Figure 6.4). She tells you it is a half-acre lot. Is she telling the truth?

   _____

6. As a building contractor, you buy the land shown in Figure 6.5. You want to divide the land into one-acre lots with a road connecting Seabury Way and Apple Avenue. Draw lines on the map to show how you would you divide the land.

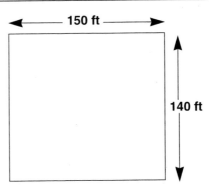

Figure 6.4 This rectangular plot is advertised as a 1⁄2-acre lot. Is the ad accurate?

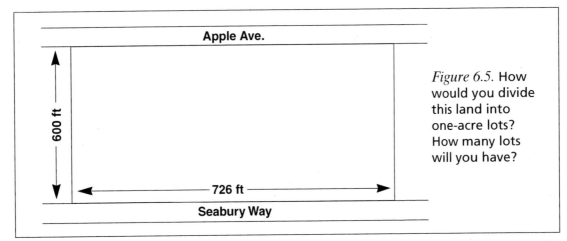

Figure 6.5. How would you divide this land into one-acre lots? How many lots will you have?

       Middle School Math You Really Need

(continued)

32. **Math and Property** (*continued*)

7. A contractor has bought a piece of land. You have hired a surveyor to measure off building lots on the land. The surveyor returns with the map shown in Figure 6.6.

   The contractor asks you to label the lots, a through j, with the proper areas in both square feet and acres. What is the area of each lot?

   a. _____

   b. _____

   c. _____

   d. _____

   e. _____

   f. _____

   g. _____

   h. _____

   i. _____

   j. _____

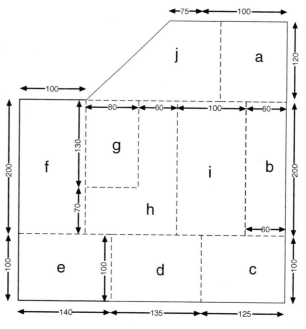

Figure 6.6. This map shows a plot of land that has been divided into 10 building lots. All numbers shown indicate distance in feet.

8. In 1862, Congress passed the Homestead Act. According to this Act, the government would give 160 acres of land to any settler who would agree to farm the land for five years.

   a. What is the area of 160 acres in square feet?

   _____

   b. This land could, and often was, given as a square plot of land. Using your pocket calculator, how would you find the length of such a square piece of land?

   _____

   _____

(continued)

                   Middle School Math You Really Need

32. **Math and Property** *(continued)*

c. What is the length, in feet, of a square plot of land containing 6,969,600 sq ft?

_____

d. What is the length, in miles, of a square plot of land that contains 6,969,600 square feet or 160 square rods?

_____

e. What is the area of the land plots, in square miles, that were offered to citizens by the Homestead Act?

_____

f. The land available through the Homestead Act was often divided into plots of one square mile each. How many acres were in such a plot? How many settlers could occupy each square mile?

Number of acres: _____

Number of settlers: _____

Name _____ Date _____

33. Prime Numbers

Prime numbers are numbers that have no factors other than themselves and one. This means there are no whole numbers, other than 1 and the number itself, that can be divided into a prime number without leaving a remainder. For example, 7 is a prime number. It can only be divided by 1, which gives 7, or by 7, which gives 1. The number 3 is not a factor of 7 because $7 \div 3 = 2.3333\ldots$ which is not a whole number. Similarly, 2, 4, 5, 6, 8, and 9 are not factors of 7.

The prime numbers, in order, from 1 to 37 are: 2, 3, 5, 7, 11, 13, 17, 19, 23, 29, 31, and 37. Prime numbers can be fun to think about, and they are important to mathematicians who study number theory.

If you are working in groups, divide into pairs. Each pair can then work to find answers for questions 1, 2, 3, and 4. Then gather in your larger group to compare your answers and work out any differences you may have. Repeat the same procedure for the rest of the questions.

1. List, in order, the prime numbers between 38 and 101.

2. The numbers 3 and 5, 5 and 7, 11 and 13, 17 and 19 are often called twin primes. This is because they lie directly before and after an intermediate number that is not a prime number. For example, 3 and 5 are twin primes that come immediately before and after the number 4. List, in order, the twin prime numbers from 5 to 38.

   _____   _____

3. List, in order, the numbers that that lie between the twin prime numbers you listed in question 2.

   _____   _____

   _____   _____

4. Name two things that the numbers you listed in question 3 have in common.

   _____

   _____

5. List, in order, all the twin prime numbers between 38 and 110.

   _____   _____

   _____   _____

   _____   _____

(continued)

33. Prime Numbers *(continued)*

6. List, in order, the numbers that lie between the twin prime numbers you listed in question 5.

   _____   _____

   _____   _____

   _____   _____

7. Do the numbers that you listed in question 6 have the same things in common that you found in question 4? If not, what is different?

   _____

   _____

8. a. Why is 2 a prime number?

   _____

   _____

   b. Do you think 2 is the only even prime number? Provide evidence to support your answer.

   _____

   _____

9. a. Why is 5 a prime number?

   _____

   _____

   b. Do you think any other number ending in 5, such as 15, 25, 35, . . . can be a prime number? Provide evidence to support your answer.

   _____

   _____

10. a. Show that if any prime number from 5 to 101 is increased or decreased by 1, one of the results will be divisible by 6.

   _____

   b. Show that this rule also applies to at least some numbers greater than 101.

   _____

   c. Show that this rule does not apply to prime numbers less than five.

   _____

11. Why must all prime numbers with 2 or more digits end in 1, 3, 7, or 9?

   _____

   _____

34. Scaling

We come across examples of scaling every day. Scaling means adjusting according to a proportion. A map is an example of scaling. On a map a kilometer may be represented by a centimeter, or a mile by 1/4 inch, and so on.

▼ ▼ ▼ ▼ ▼ ▼ ▼ ▼ ▼ ▼ ▼ ▼ ▼ ▼ ▼ ▼ ▼ ▼

If you are working in groups, divide into pairs and do the scaling suggested in the problems that follow. Each pair can then work together to find answers for questions 1, 2, 3, and 4. Then gather in groups of four to compare your answers and work out any differences you may have.

▼ ▼ ▼ ▼ ▼ ▼ ▼ ▼ ▼ ▼ ▼ ▼ ▼ ▼ ▼ ▼ ▼ ▼

1. A dollar bill is six inches long. "If the national deficit of 1990, of 220.469 billion dollars, were to be laid out, dollar by dollar, it would stretch from here to __." Find how far the bills would extend. Then try to suggest some distance that is about the same.

    Length: _____

    "From here to _____."

2. The earth is 8,000 miles in diameter. The sun is almost 1,000,000 miles in diameter. "If the earth were the size of an orange, the sun would be the size of __. " Find the number and one or more things that might represent the sun.

    Diameter: _____

    "The sun would be the size of _____."

3. New York is 2,466 miles from Los Angeles and Chicago is 727 miles from New York. "If the distance from New York to Los Angeles took only an hour to fly, it would take __ of an hour to fly from New York to Chicago." Fill in the missing words.

    "It would take _____ of an hour."

4. Belgium covers 11,781 square miles. India's area is 1,269,339 square miles. The population of Belgium is 10,000,000. The population of India is 685,000,000. "If all the people of India were to move to Belgium, there would be __ people in every square mile." Fill in the missing numbers in people per square mile.

    People per square mile: _____

         Middle School Math You Really Need

35. Velocity from Distance and Time

If you are riding in the front seat of a car, you can tell how fast you are going by reading the speedometer. If you are riding in a bus or in the back seat of a car or van, you may not be able to see the speedometer. A law-enforcement officer can determine a vehicle's speed with a radar gun. You probably don't have a radar gun, but you can still make a good estimate of a vehicle's speed. Using a pencil, a pad, a hand-held calculator, and a watch with a second hand, you can determine the speed of vehicles in which you are traveling even if you can't see the speedometer. If you add a measuring tape to your equipment, you can determine the speed of vehicles that are moving along a road near your home or school.

Suppose that you are traveling along a highway. You may see distance indicators such as mile posts or signs that give the distance to cities or towns that lie ahead. Write down the time and distance as you pass a mile post or a sign that gives the distance to a town or city that you are approaching.

For example, you record the distance on a sign that reads, "Kansas City 30 miles." At the same moment, you record the time on your watch, which might be 1:35 and 20 seconds. When you pass another sign that reads, "Kansas City 20 miles," the time according to your watch is 1:45 and 30 seconds. To find the average speed of the vehicle in which you are riding, divide the distance traveled by the time in minutes. In this case:

$$\frac{30 \text{ mi} - 20 \text{ mi}}{10 \text{ min} + 10 \text{ s}} = \frac{10 \text{ mi}}{10 + {}^{10}\!/_{60} \text{ min}} = \frac{10 \text{ mi}}{10.17 \text{ min.}} = 0.98 \text{ mi/min}$$

To convert miles per minute (mi/min) to miles per hour (mph), you need to multiply by 60 minutes per hour (min/h) because:

$$\frac{1 \text{ mi}}{\cancel{\text{min}}} \times \frac{60 \ \cancel{\text{min}}}{\text{h}} = \frac{60 \text{ mi}}{\text{h}}$$

A speed of:

$$\frac{0.98 \text{ mi}}{\cancel{\text{min}}} \times \frac{60 \text{ min}}{\text{h}} = 59 \text{ mph}$$

(continued)

35. Velocity from Distance and Time *(continued)*

▼ ▼ ▼ ▼ ▼ ▼ ▼ ▼ ▼ ▼ ▼ ▼ ▼ ▼ ▼ ▼ ▼ ▼ ▼

If you are working in groups, divide into pairs and do the first two problems together. Then gather in groups of four to compare your answers and work out any differences you may have.

Your teacher will make recommendations about the activities described in question 3.

▼ ▼ ▼ ▼ ▼ ▼ ▼ ▼ ▼ ▼ ▼ ▼ ▼ ▼ ▼ ▼ ▼ ▼ ▼

1. You pass a mile post that indicates "62 miles." Sixty-eight seconds later you pass another marker that reads "61 miles." What is the average speed, in miles per hour, of the vehicle in which you are riding?

   _____

2. A car passes a sign that reads "Dallas 95 miles." A passenger in the car records the time, which is 10:30 and 25 seconds. Later the car passes a sign that reads, "Dallas 65 miles." What was the car's average speed if the passenger's watch now indicates:

   a. 10:58 and 38 seconds? _____

   b. 11:20 and 38 seconds? _____

   c. What type of road would you guess the car was traveling on based on the result you found in part a? On the result you found in part b?

   _____

   _____

3. You can measure the speed of vehicles traveling along a road near your school or home. BUT BE SURE TO: (1) STAY A SAFE DISTANCE FROM THE ROAD and (2) ASK YOUR TEACHER OR PARENTS FOR PERMISSION!

   Use a measuring tape to find the distance between two trees, posts, poles, signs, or other markers located a safe distance from the road. These two markers should be several hundred feet (50 meters or more) apart. As a vehicle crosses the first marker, raise your hand to signal your partner and immediately start a stopwatch or note the position of the second hand on your watch. Your partner, standing beside the second marker, signals you when the same vehicle passes his or her position.

   (continued)

35. Velocity from Distance and Time *(continued)*

From the measured distance and the time, in seconds, you can find the vehicle's speed. For example, suppose the markers are 300 feet (91.5 m) apart and the time for a car to travel from the first marker to the second is 7.0 seconds. The car's speed would be:

300 ft ÷ 7.0 s = 43 ft/s (13 m/s)

To change this speed to miles per hour (mph) or kilometers per hour (kph), you must convert feet to miles (or meters to kilometers) and seconds to hours. This is not difficult if you know there are 5,280 feet in a mile (or 1,000 meters in a kilometer) and 3,600 seconds (60 s/min × 60 min/ h) in an hour. In this case you would find:

$$\frac{43 \text{ ft}}{\text{s}} \times \frac{1 \text{ mi}}{5280 \text{ ft}} \times \frac{3600 \text{ s}}{\text{h}} = 29 \text{ mph}$$

or

$$\frac{13 \text{ m}}{\text{s}} \times \frac{1 \text{ km}}{1000 \text{ m}} \times \frac{3600 \text{ s}}{\text{h}} = 47 \text{ kph}$$

Now make your measurements of the speeds of vehicles traveling along the road where you have set up your experiment.

a. Do any of the vehicles exceed the speed limit along this road?

_____

b. Can you use this experiment to measure the speed of cyclists and people walking beside the road?

_____

c. Ask an adult to drive a car at a steady speed past your markers. Calculate the car's speed and compare your results with the driver. How closely does your calculation agree with the car's speedometer?

_____

_____

36. Are Negative Numbers Ever Real?

Negative numbers are as real as positive numbers. Think of the daily temperature, for example. In the United States, we use the Fahrenheit temperature scale. If it is just at the freezing point, we say it is 32° F. In Europe, where they use the Celsius scale, the same temperature is 0°C. When the Fahrenheit temperature drops to 10°F, a Parisian will tell you it is -12° C. The negative sign is a result of choosing different, but equivalent, scales for temperature. Two thermometers, one with the Celsius and one with the Fahrenheit scale, are shown to the right (Figure 6.7). The scales have been placed so that the freezing and boiling points for water are side by side.

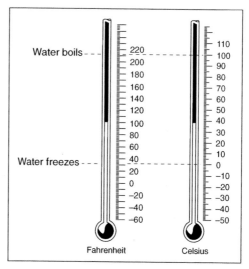

Figure 6.7. Celsius and Fahrenheit temperature scales

▼ ▼ ▼ ▼ ▼ ▼ ▼ ▼ ▼ ▼ ▼ ▼ ▼ ▼ ▼ ▼ ▼

If you are working in groups, divide into pairs. Each individual can try to answer the questions that follow. After writing your answers, compare them with your partner and work out any differences you may have. Once you reach agreement, meet in the larger group to compare answers and work out any differences.

▼ ▼ ▼ ▼ ▼ ▼ ▼ ▼ ▼ ▼ ▼ ▼ ▼ ▼ ▼ ▼ ▼

1. On a very cold day it is –18°F. What is the temperature on a Celsius thermometer?

   _____

2. When it is –40°C in Antarctica, what is the equivalent temperature on a Fahrenheit thermometer?

   _____

3. The following temperatures were taken at noon in Paris. In New York they would be reported in degrees Fahrenheit. What would be the noontime temperatures in Paris as reported in New York?

(continued)

36. Are Negative Numbers Ever Real? *(continued)*

Paris Noon Temperature	New York Report	Paris Noon Temperature	New York Report
20°C	____°F	12°C	____°F
35°C	____°F	5°C	____°F
–10°C	____°F	–5°C	____°F

4. The following temperatures were taken at noon in Dallas. In Rome they would be reported in degrees Celsius. What would the noontime temperatures in Dallas as reported in Rome be?

Dallas Noon Temperature	Rome Report	Dallas Noon Temperature	Rome Report
80°F	____°C	102°F	____°C
35°F	____°C	12°F	____°C
–10°F	____°C	–25°F	____°C

We often assign negative numbers to debts. For example, if a bank has $80,000,000 in assets and $1,000,000 in debts, its net worth is $80,000,000 – $1,000,000 = $79,000,000. To find the total $1,000,000 in debts, all of the individual debts could be listed as negative numbers. All of the individual assets making up the $80,000,000 could be listed as positive numbers.

5. An accounting firm lists the following assets and debts for a business:

Assets	
cash on hand	$1,000,000
bank savings account	$32,000,000

Debts	
outstanding bills	$2,000,000
salaries due	$1,500,000
unpaid bills	$3,500,000

What is the net worth of this business?

37. Handheld Calculators

There are many different types of handheld calculators. Different models have a different number and variety of functions.

For example, Texas Instruments makes a number of different calculators. Two of them are the TI-30 and the TI-1766.

The TI-1766 is a fairly simple instrument. The operations that it can perform are addition, subtraction, multiplication, division, square root, percentage and various types of memory storage.

The TI-30 is a more complicated instrument. In addition to the operations performed by the TI-1766, it can find reciprocals, sines, cosines, tangents, logs, lns, and powers.

Let's look at the power function. It is indicated on the key as y^x.

This means that the number y is to be raised to the power x. For example, 3^4 can be found by first pressing the button labeled "3" to enter the number 3 on the screen. Next you enter y^x by pressing that button, then you enter 4 and press the equal button. The number 81, which equals $3 \times 3 \times 3 \times 3$, will appear on the screen.

The beauty of the y^x key is that it will raise any number including decimal numbers to any power including decimal powers.

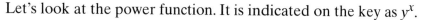

If you are working in groups, divide into pairs. Each pair can then work together to find answers for questions 1-8. Then do questions 9 and 10 by yourself. Check 9 and 10 with your partner before you meet in the larger group to compare answers and work out any differences.

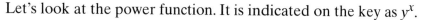

Here are some practice problems to help you become familiar with the y^x function on a handheld calculator.

1. $12^3 =$ _____

2. $2^5 =$ _____

3. $4^6 =$ _____

4. $3.14^5 =$ _____

(continued)

37. **Handheld Calculators** (continued)

5. $12^{3.1} =$ _____

6. $2.01^{5.02} =$ _____

7. $1.54^{17.7} =$ _____

8. $7.54^{4.2376} =$ _____

Compound interest is found in banks by using prepared tables. The tables are based on the formula $S = P(1 + r)^t$. Here **S** is the sum of the principal and the interest, **P** is the principal, **r** is the rate of interest, and **t** is the number of interest periods. (Be sure to change any interest expressed as percent to hundredths when you put r into this formula.)

9. A depositor opens an account with a principal of $10,000. The bank agrees to pay compound interest at a rate of 4.65% annually. How much will the money be worth at the end of ten years?

_____

10. What is the value of $18,000 compounded quarterly (every 3 months) at 4.0% annual interest for three and a half years?

_____

     Middle School Math You Really Need

38. Photographic Light Meters

A fully automatic camera is easy to use. You aim the camera and push a button. The camera focuses, opens the shutter to let light in, and closes again. These cameras are great for taking snapshots. But they don't give the photographer any control over how the picture will look.

People who want to be able to control the image usually don't use automatic cameras. They use cameras that let them adjust how much light comes in through the camera lens, and how quickly the shutter opens and closes again.

The lens on a camera is a little like the pupils of your eyes. It has an opening that can be made much larger or smaller. When the opening is small, it only lets in a little light—like your pupils on a very bright day. When the opening is large, it lets in a lot of light—like your pupils in a dim room.

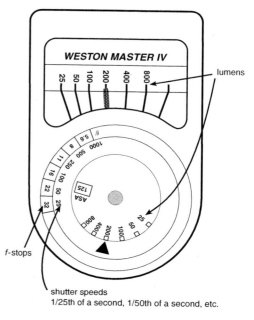

Figure 6.8. A light meter like this one is useful to a photographer.

To tell how big the **aperture**, or opening, of the lens should be, photographers need to know how much light is available. For this they use a light meter.

Light meters can be built into the camera, or they can be handheld. The meter tells the photographer which combinations of shutter speed and aperture opening are possible with the amount of light available.

Figure 6.8 shows a light meter. The meter is aimed at the object being photographed. The scale marked "Weston Master IV" gives the intensity of the light, in **lumens**, received by the meter. This intensity is then set on the innermost ring of the meter. The possible shutter speed and lens opening combinations are shown on the two outer dials.

For any given light intensity, several combinations of shutter speed and opening are possible. For example, an intensity of 200 is shown on the meter in Figure 6.8. (The film speed has been set at 125 in the window marked "ASA.") The possible combinations of shutter speed and aperture opening, or f-stops, are f/32 at 1/25 s, f/22 at 1/50 s, f/16 at 1/100 s, etc. These all admit the same amount of light to the film. This is because the aperture openings double in size as they go from f/32 to f/22, to f/16.

(continued)

38. Photographic Light Meters *(continued)*

If the shutter speed changes from 1/25 s to 1/50 s, half as much light will enter the camera because the shutter is open half as long. To compensate for the reduced light admitted when the shutter speed halves, the photographer can change the aperture opening from f/32 to f/22. This doubles the size of the aperture, and the amount of light admitted. As a result, the two settings admit the same amount of light. Thus f/32 at 1/25 s is equivalent to f/22 at 1/50 s.

The reason for choosing a different combination may be related to the speed of the object being photographed. To catch motion that would be blurred at 1/25 s, the photographer can use faster shutter speeds such as 1/500 s and increase the size of the aperture.

The important things to know are:

1. The scale marked "Weston Master IV" shows the intensity of the light received from the subject to be photographed. The numbers 25, 50, 100, 200, 400, 800, and 1600 simply mean that 50 is twice as much light as 25, 100 is twice as much light as 50, etc.

2. The shutter speeds are 1/1000 s, 1/500 s, 1/ 250 s, . . . 1/2 s, 1 s, 2 s, 4 s, . . . (Notice that half of 1/500 s is 1/1000 s, not 1/250 s).

3. The aperture opening is given by "f" numbers. These are f/1.4, f/2, f/2.8, f/4, f/5.6, f/8, f/11, f/16, f/22 and f/32. Each f-stop gives an opening half the size of the one before it. The bigger the f/number, the smaller the opening! The opening at f/22 is half the size of the opening at f/16 and twice the size of the opening at f/32.

4. Different films react more quickly to light. A film with a rating of ASA 250 reacts to light twice as quickly as one with a rating of ASA 125. This means that the shutter only needs to be open half as long.

▼ ▼ ▼ ▼ ▼ ▼ ▼ ▼ ▼ ▼ ▼ ▼ ▼ ▼ ▼ ▼ ▼ ▼

If you are working in groups, divide into pairs. Each pair can then work together to find answers for the questions that follow. After answering the questions, meet in the larger group to compare answers and methods of solution. Try to work out any differences in answers that may exist within the group.

▼ ▼ ▼ ▼ ▼ ▼ ▼ ▼ ▼ ▼ ▼ ▼ ▼ ▼ ▼ ▼ ▼ ▼

(continued)

38. Photographic Light Meters *(continued)*

1. A shutter speed of 1/500 s is needed to stop the motion in a picture that shows the meter readings of Figure 6.8. What f-number should be used?

    _____

2. A film with speed ASA 250 is to be used instead of ASA 125. What setting of the shutter speed will be needed at f/16?

    _____

3. Suppose we want to double the exposure time for a scene that indicates 1/50 s at f/11. What f-number should we use at a shutter speed of 1/100 s?

    _____

4. A photo taken on ASA 125 film shows a light intensity of 1/50 at f/22. What would be the equivalent reading at f/16, using much faster film, ASA 1000?

    _____

5. If the intensity of light on the meter shown in Figure 6.8 increased from 200 to 400, what shutter speed should be used for an aperture setting of f/16?

    _____

To the Teacher

The problems in this chapter will help students to see that mathematics is used in the arts as well as in the sciences and social sciences. You might ask your colleagues who teach art or music for other examples and encourage them to point out these uses to their students as they arise.

39. *Math in Art* (page 125)

Answers

1. Each small patch needs an extra $\frac{1}{4}$ inch on all sides or a patch $3\frac{1}{2}$ inches square. For all nine patches, a cloth $10\frac{1}{2}$ in. × $10\frac{1}{2}$ in. is required.

2. The 3 yards of 52-inch-wide material is 108 in × 52 in. Figure T7.1a shows how 10 pieces of 20-inch × 24-inch canvas can be cut from the larger piece. (A 16- × 20-inch piece needs to be 20 × 24 inches to allow for 2-inch stapling edges on all sides.) There will be a 4-inch waste piece on the edge and an 8-inch waste piece at the end of the 3 yard cut.

   Figure T7.1b shows how 12 small patches can be cut from the 60-inch-wide material. It will have a 12-inch-wide waste piece on the end and no waste on the side.

3. The 52-inch canvas cost $18 x 3 = $54 and made 10 patches, or $54/10 = $5.40

per patch. The 60-inch material cost $20 × 3 = $60, or $60/12 = $5.00 per patch.

4. The paper's 26-inch dimension restricts the painting to three times the size of the sketch, since 3 × 7 in. = 21 in will fit, but four times this side (28 inches) is too big. A painting three times the size of the sketch will be 12 in × 21 in.

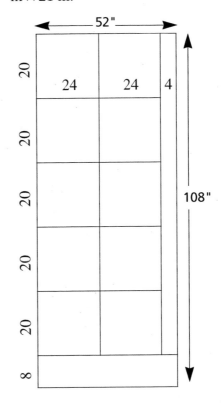

10 canvases at $18/yard = $54
$5.40 per canvas

Figure T7.1a

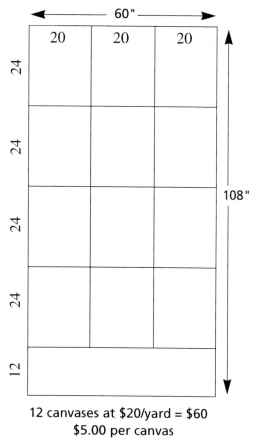

60"

20   20   20

24

24

108"

24

24

12

12 canvases at $20/yard = $60
$5.00 per canvas

Figure T7.1b

40. *Mathematics in Music* (page 127)

To give the student an understanding of the sound created by the frequencies dealt with in this chapter, you might ask a student who plays a stringed instrument to bring it to class. By dividing any vibrating string in half, the students will be able to hear the frequency doubled. Take the total length of any string and mark exactly the points corresponding to a half, a fourth, a fifth, a sixth, and a seventh of that length. If a finger is placed very firmly on each of these points and the bow pulled or the string plucked quickly, the student will create frequencies 2, 4, 5, 6, and 7 times the frequencies of the entire string. These are called natural harmonics.

On a C string these frequencies will be given by:

$$66 \times 2 = 132 \qquad 66 \times 6 = 396$$
$$66 \times 4 = 264 \qquad 66 \times 7 = 462$$
$$66 \times 5 = 330 \qquad 66 \times 8 = 528$$

The frequencies above correspond to the notes C, C, E, G, B flat, and C. The students will recognize the typical sounds used in a trumpet revelry (the trumpet divides the vibrating air column just as the harmonics sounding on the divided string). These are the first, third, fifth, and minor seventh degrees of the C major scale. They are the basis of western musical melody and harmony. Any student who plays the guitar can play a C major chord and a C dominant 7th chord, sounding the notes one by one to let the class hear that these are the same notes created by the natural harmonics on the C string or the trumpet.

The student can be asked to find the ratio between notes in the C major scale (questions 2–6). These ratios will not all be perfect (not all the fifths will be 1.5 exactly, etc.) because the frequencies derived from the natural harmonics of a string have been adjusted to satisfy the tuning of a piano or an orchestra in music that covers a vast gamut of scales.

The frequencies found by dividing the string's length by 2, 3, 5, and 7 create the intervals of an octave, a third, a fifth, and a minor seventh respectively, with ratios of 2, 1.25, 1.5, and 1.75. These frequencies can be found on various strings creating various chords. (The A string will create C sharp, E, and G; the D string, F sharp, A, and C, etc.) When the students hear the notes on the violin, viola, or cello string and the chords on the guitar, they will understand the relationship between the mathematical progression and western harmony.

Some students may wonder why some notes are designated sharp (#) and flat (♭).

To understand why F-sharp (F#) is so designated, notice that the difference in frequency between F and G on the C major scale is:

(396 – 352) vib/sec = 44 vib/sec.

Adding half this difference, 22 vib/sec to the frequency of F gives:

(352 + 22) vib/sec = 374 vib/sec.

This is just about the frequency designated for F#. We say that F has been raised a half-interval, or *half-tone,* to F#. We could also say that G has been lowered a half-tone to G-flat (G♭). Similarly, C# or D♭ lie about halfway between C (528 vib/sec) and D (594 vib/sec).

Answers

1. An octave above middle C the frequency is 528 vib/sec. At an octave below middle C, the frequency is 132 vib/sec.

2, 3, 4, and 5 for the C major scale:

Note	Frequency	Fifth	Fourth	Third	Sixth
C	264				
D	297				
E	330			1.25	
F	352		1.33	1.19	
G	396	1.50	1.33	1.20	
A	440	1.48	1.33	1.25	1.67
B	495	1.50	1.40	1.25	1.67
C	528	1.50	1.33	1.20	1.60
		3/2	4/3	5/4	5/3
		5th	4th	3rd	6th

6. D major diatonic scale:

Note	Frequency	Fifth	Fourth	Third	Sixth
D	297				
E	334				
F#	371			1.25	
G	396		1.33	1.19	
A	445	1.50	1.33	1.20	
B	495	1.48	1.33	1.25	1.66
C#	557	1.50	1.41	1.25	1.66
D	594	1.50	1.33	1.20	1.60
		3/2	4/3	5/4	5/3
		5th	4th	3rd	6th

7. For the C Major Scale (Only one octave is included.)

Scale Note	Freq. (vib/sec)	Diff.	Ratios
C	264		
D	297	33	1.125
E	330	33	1.111
F	352	22	1.067
G	396	44	1.125
A	440	44	1.111
B	495	55	1.125
C	528	33	1.067

For the D major scale. (Only one octave is included.)

Scale Note	Freq. (vib/sec)	Diff.	Ratios
D	297		
E	334	37	1.125
F#	371	37	1.111
G	396	25	1.067
A	445	49	1.124
B	495	50	1.112
C#	557	62	1.125
D	594	37	1.067

8. The ratios of the tones of the C and D major scales are the same. Notice that the *differences* in the frequencies of the two scales do not form a pattern.

9. The C major and the D major scales are adjusted so that the pattern of ratios (not the differences) of the scale notes are the same and the ratios of the intervals (fifths, fourths, thirds and sixths) are the same.

41. *The Mathematics of Rhythm*

This is a class exercise; consequently, there are no written instructions for the students.

The two principal elements of music are rhythm and melody—the basic patterns found in western music. It is important to note that music is a language and that the musical patterns you explore here are typical to western music. In other cultures, melodies and rhythms follow patterns, but not necessarily the same patterns found in western music.

Rhythm in music is always relative. Conventional notation doesn't establish how long a note lasts, but rather the time a note lasts compared to another note. So all of note-reading has to do with comparing the lengths of notes. Starting with a whole note, which can last any length of time, we find it equal in time to two half notes, four quarter notes, eight eighth notes, or two quarter notes plus one half note, etc. If the whole note lasts one second, the half note lasts a half second, and the eighth note an eighth of a second.

It is easy to use hand claps to show these divisions quite precisely, and thereby demonstrate the most typical proportions in musical rhythms. Have half the class clap whole seconds (matching the second hand of a clock or watch) using a one syllable word, such as "CAT" to help with precision. They can say "CAT" as they bring their hands together. The other half of the class will clap two times for each second and say "TIGER," creating half seconds for each clap. The second half of the class can then divide the whole note into thirds using the word "ELEPHANT." Later, they can divide it into into fourths and use the word "CATERPILLAR." The first half of the class will keep the one second "CAT" rhythm steady throughout.

It is important to exaggerate the accent on the first syllable for precise coordination. To divide the whole note into sixths or eighths, all you have to do is say "ELEPHANT" or "CATERPILLAR" twice to each "CAT." Now start with a whole note ("CAT") that is two seconds long and clap the same divisions as before. The whole note is twice as long and the words twice as slow, but the division (half, third, fourth, etc.) are exactly the same.

Now have the class find rhythm patterns in some very well known tunes:

Jingle bells Jingle bells (.. _ .. _);
Frère Jacques Frère Jacques (........);
Baa Baa black sheep have you any wool (.... 0 0 0 0).

First clap and sing the melodies. If you clap once for each dot, you establish a constant value like we did with "CAT." As you sing , keep this constant dot value going so that you can compare it to the other values.

If the dots represent the value of a quarter note, what value do you think is represented by the dashes? By the little circles? Answer: The dashes represent a half of a whole note and the circles an eighth.

Try analyzing the rhythmic proportions in the following melodies using these symbols:

$$\_ = \frac{1}{2}, . = \frac{1}{4}, 0 = \frac{1}{8}$$

1. Fly in the buttermilk, shoo, fly, shoo! Skip to the Lou my darling. (Use "fly" as a quarter note value.)

2. Twinkle, twinkle, little star, how I wonder what you are. (Analyze this melody :

   a. using the first syllable of "twinkle" for the quarter note;

   b. using the first syllable of twinkle as the eighth note)

3. Here we go round the mulberry bush, the mulberry bush, the mulberry bush.

Answers

1. . 0 0 0 0 . . . __ . 0 0 . . __ __

2. a. . . . . . . __ . . . . . . __

   b. 0 0 0 0 0 0 . 0 0 0 0 0 0 .

3. . . . __ . . . . __ . . . . __ . . . . __

The first two rhythms have obvious accents every two or four notes. Where would you put the accents on the third melody?

39. Math in Art

Did you know that artists use mathematics in their work? Leonardo da Vinci used geometry to draw wonderful sketches of the human body. M.C. Escher used a deep understanding of perspective to produce intriguing drawings. Some of his drawings amaze the viewer with spiraling staircases that never end.

The following questions show a few ways artists use mathematics in their work. You will find other uses if you continue to study art.

▼ ▼ ▼ ▼ ▼ ▼ ▼ ▼ ▼ ▼ ▼ ▼ ▼ ▼ ▼ ▼ ▼

If you are working in groups, divide into pairs. Work individually on questions 1-4. Then compare solutions with your partner. Finally, meet in your larger group to work out any disagreements you may have.

▼ ▼ ▼ ▼ ▼ ▼ ▼ ▼ ▼ ▼ ▼ ▼ ▼ ▼ ▼ ▼ ▼

1. A quilt artist wants to make a 9-inch × 9-inch patch as shown in Figure 7.1. Each square is to be made of nine 3-inch × 3-inch smaller squares. Each 3-inch square needs a $\frac{1}{4}$-inch seam allowance on all sides so they can be sewn together. What size should the artist cut the cloth to make the small squares?

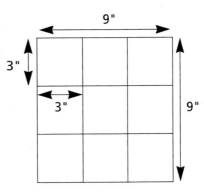

Figure 7.1. A 9-inch by 9-inch quilt pattern.

2. A painter wants to make a number of 16-inch × 20-inch canvases for separate oil paintings. Each small canvas must have 2 inches of extra material on each side so it can be stapled to the wooden stretcher. (See figure 7.2.)

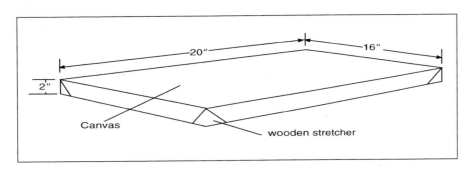

Figure 7.2. An artist's canvas on a wooden stretcher.

(continued)

Middle School Math You Really Need

39. Math in Art *(continued)*

She has a choice of buying a three-yard piece of canvas that is 52 inches wide, or a three-yard piece of canvas that is 60 inches wide.

How many canvases can be cut from the 52-inch material?

_____

From the 60-inch material?

_____

3. The 52-inch canvas costs $18 per yard. The 60-inch canvas costs $20 per yard. Which canvas would produce the least expensive stretched canvas?

_____

4. An artist wants to make a watercolor painting of a 4-inch × 7-inch sketch. He wants to keep the same proportions as in the sketch, but plans to paint on a sheet of paper that is 16 inches × 26 inches. What is the largest painting (in whole inches) that he can make on this size paper, while keeping the same proportions?

_____

40. Mathematics in Music

Musicians also use mathematics in their work. Pythagoras, a Greek philosopher who was born around 500 B.C., realized that the Earth was a giant sphere. He also discovered that the **frequency** (pitch) of a vibrating string depends on its length. Halving the length of a violin string raises its pitch by one octave. Musicians have been using mathematics ever since Pythagoras.

The scale used for music in the Western Hemisphere is divided into seven tones, A, B, C, D, E, F, and G.

Whenever a string of a guitar, piano, or any other musical instrument vibrates at 440 times per second, we say that the instrument is sounding the tone, or pitch, of a note called middle A.

What happens if we strike a key on the piano that vibrates 880 times per second? This note, when sounded with the 440-vibrations-per-second string, gives a pleasing sensation. We say the notes are *harmonious.* A note of 220 vibrations per second and a note with 440 vibrations per second are also harmonious. It is customary to call the note associated with 440 vibrations per second middle A. We call a note associated with 880 vibrations per second an octave above middle A. We call a note associated with 220 vibrations per second an octave below middle A. You can play harmonious notes on a stringed instrument by simply playing the whole string followed by playing the same string at half its length. The half string will vibrate at twice the frequency of the whole string. Therefore, it will sound the higher-pitched note.

The C major scale starts at middle C, 264 vibrations per second. (See Table 7.1.)

Vocal	Note	Scale Note Frequency (vib/sec)
do	C	264
re	D	297
mi	E	330
fa	F	352
sol	G	396
la	A	440
ti	B	495
do	C	528

Table 7.1: The C Major Scale (Only one octave is included.)

(continued)

         Middle School Math You Really Need

40. **Mathematics in Music** *(continued)*

▼ ▼ ▼ ▼ ▼ ▼ ▼ ▼ ▼ ▼ ▼ ▼ ▼ ▼ ▼ ▼ ▼ ▼ ▼ ▼

If you are working in groups, divide into pairs and work together to solve the first 8 questions. Then meet in your larger group to compare solutions and work out any differences you may have. The larger group can then work together on question 9, which involves bringing together all that you have learned in the first 8 questions.

▼ ▼ ▼ ▼ ▼ ▼ ▼ ▼ ▼ ▼ ▼ ▼ ▼ ▼ ▼ ▼ ▼ ▼ ▼

1. Name the frequency of each note.

   a. An octave above middle C _____

   b. An octave below middle C _____

2. a. Find the ratio of the frequency of the fifth note of the C major scale, G, to the frequency of first note of the scale, C. To find the ratio, divide the first number (frequency of G) by the second number (frequency of C).

      _____

   b. Find the ratio of the frequency of the sixth note, A, to the frequency of the second note, D.

      _____

   c. Then find the ratio of the frequency of the seventh note to the third note and the eighth note to the fourth note. (Reduce these ratios to the simplest fraction.)

      _____

   d. These ratios (or intervals) are called *fifths*, because they are five notes apart. Are the ratios of fifths exactly the same? Are they very nearly the same?

      _____

3. Find the ratios of the frequencies of *fourths* notes that are four notes apart.

   _____

4. Find the ratios of the frequencies of *thirds*. _____

(continued)

40. Mathematics in Music *(continued)*

5. What are the ratios of *sixths*? _____

6. Do questions 2 through 5 for the D major scale shown in Table 7.2.

Table 7.2: The D major scale. (Only one octave is included.)

Vocal	Note	Scale Note Frequency (vib/sec)
do	D	297
re	E	334
mi	F#	371
fa	G	396
sol	A	445
la	B	495
ti	C#	557
do	D	594

7. Make tables showing the ratios of tones for successive notes in the C major and D major scales. That is, find the ratio of the frequency for D to the frequency for C, and the same for E to D, F to E, and so on. On the same tables, show the difference in frequency for successive notes (frequency for D minus frequency for C, and so on.)

8. a. How do the ratios for the two scales compare?

   b. How do the differences in frequency compare?

9. How are major scales formed?